Contents

Shapes and Sorting

Shapes and Patterns

Numbers Through 5 and Plane Figures

Data and Graphs

Numbers Through 20

xi

Add or Subtract: Problem Solving

Measurement

Numbers Through 30

Solid Figures

Identify Plane Figures
Look for Shapes

Color each shape.

Then cut out the shapes.

L E A R N

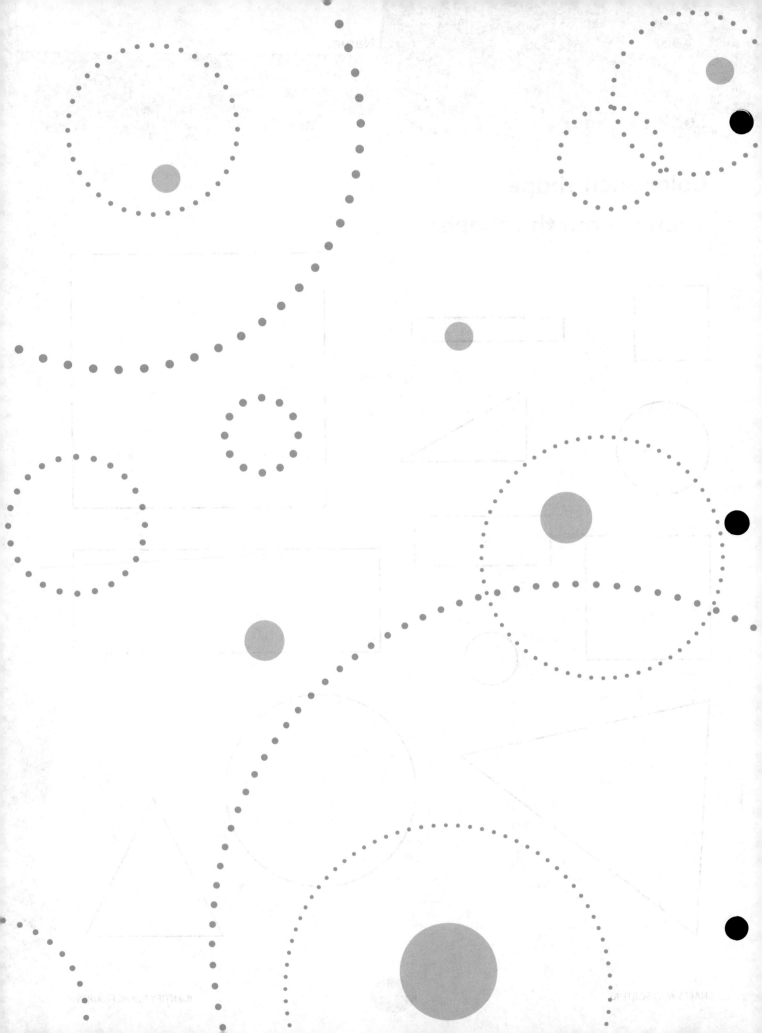

Identify Plane Figures
Shapes Are Everywhere

Color the shapes in the picture. Use these colors.

circles
red

rectangles
yellow

triangles
green

squares
blue

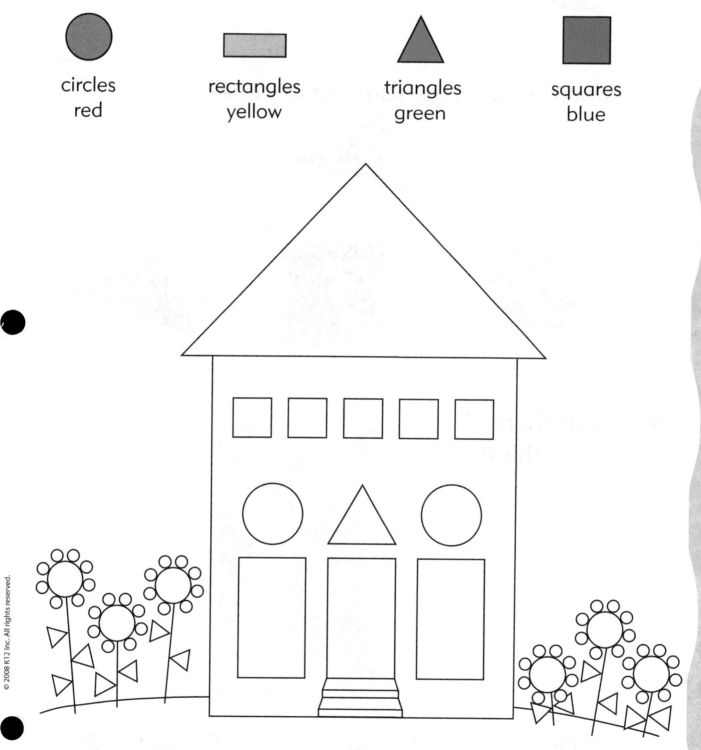

3

TRY IT

Read each problem and circle the answer.

1. Which shape is a square?

A.

B.

C.

2. Which shape is the same as this one?

A.

B.

C.

3. What shape do you see on this door?

A. circle   B. square   C. rectangle

TRY IT

Name:

Color each shape. Then cut out the shapes.

L E A R N

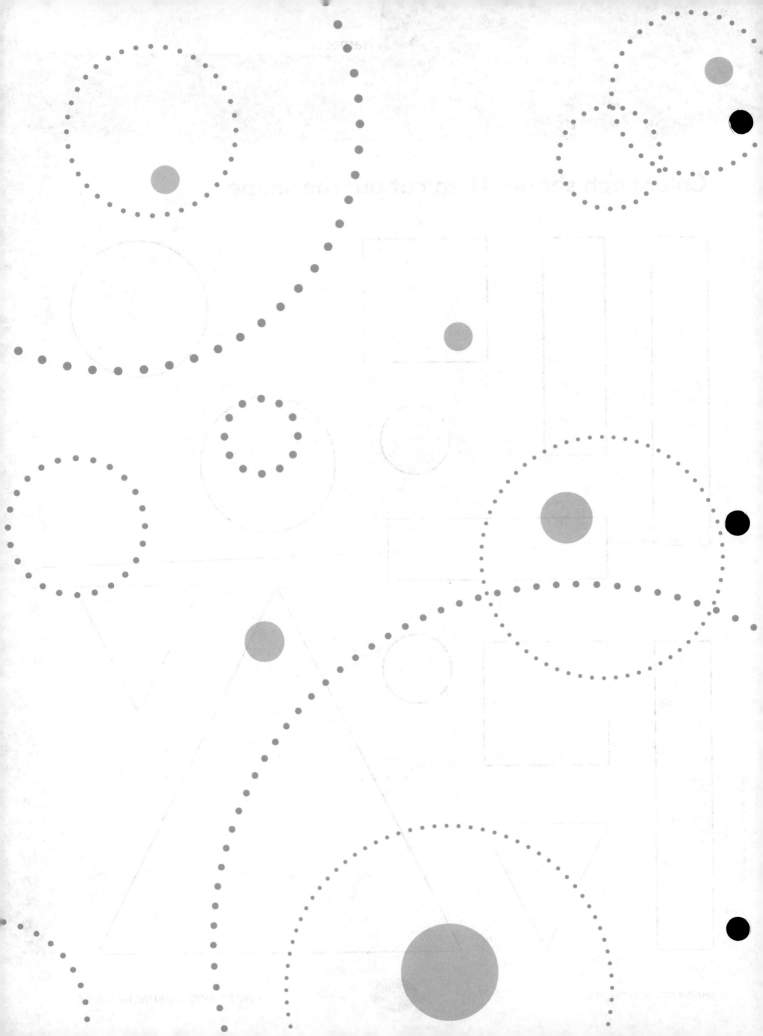

Circle, Triangle, Square, Rectangle

Common Shapes

1. Circle the shape that is a circle.

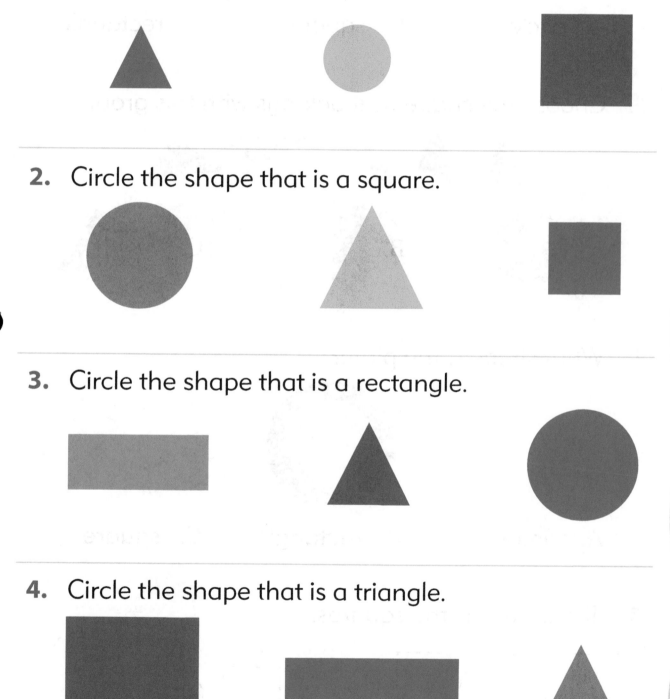

2. Circle the shape that is a square.

3. Circle the shape that is a rectangle.

4. Circle the shape that is a triangle.

TRY IT

For Problems 5–7, circle the answer.

5. What is the shape of these objects?

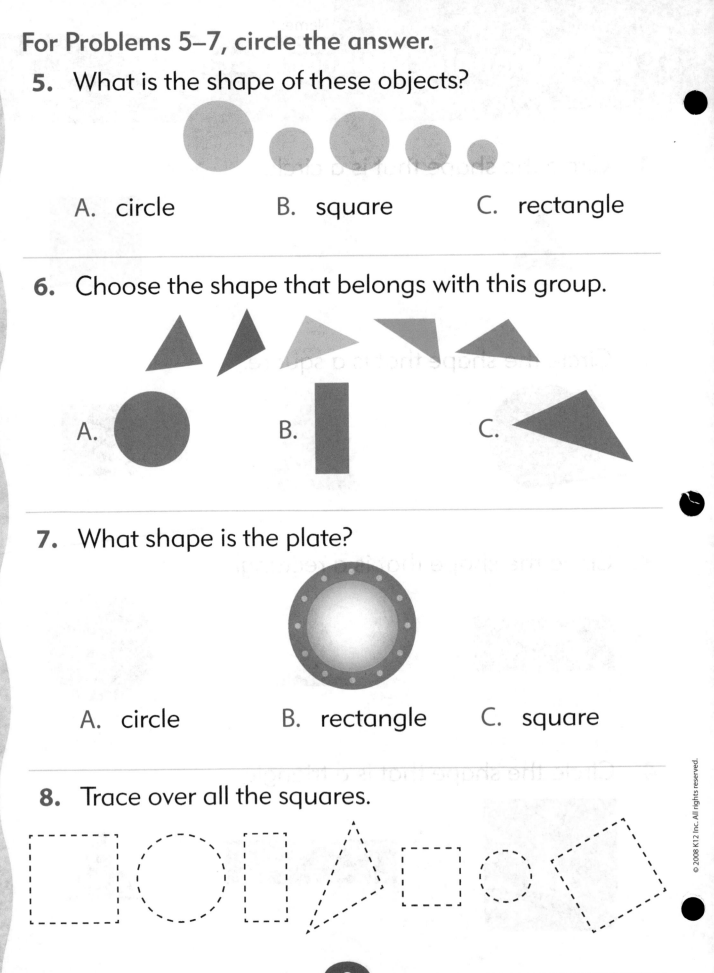

A. circle   B. square   C. rectangle

6. Choose the shape that belongs with this group.

A.   B.   C.

7. What shape is the plate?

A. circle   B. rectangle   C. square

8. Trace over all the squares.

TRY IT

Compare Shapes

Shape Match

Look at the shape on the basket. Then look at the shapes in the row next to the basket. Circle the shape in the row that is the same as the shape on the basket.

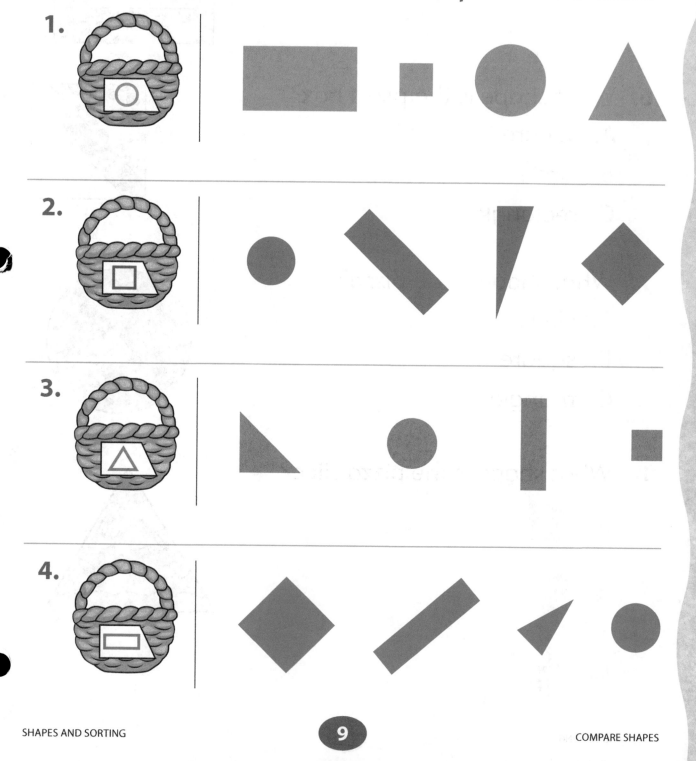

TRY IT

Read each problem and circle the answer.

5. What shape is the oven door?

   A. square

   B. rectangle

   C. triangle

6. What shape is the pizza box?

   A. square

   B. circle

   C. rectangle

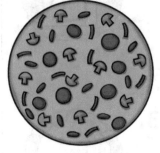

7. What shape is the pizza?

   A. circle

   B. square

   C. triangle

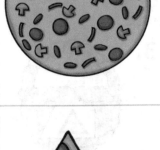

8. What shape is the pizza slice?

   A.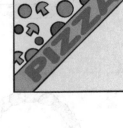

   B.

   C.

T R Y   I T

Compare Colors

Same Colors

Look at the objects in each row.
Circle the objects that are the same color.

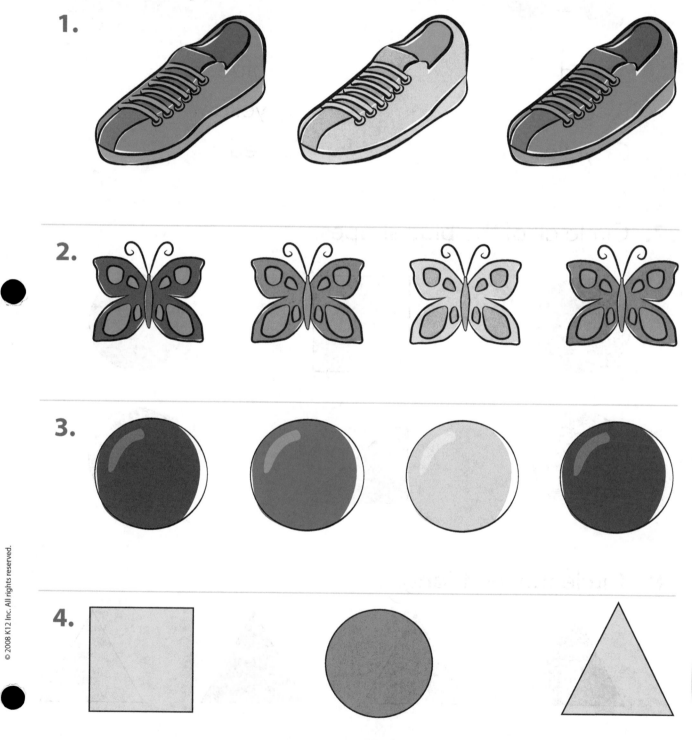

1.

2.

3.

4.

T R Y   I T

Read each problem and circle the answer.

5. What color is the frog?

A. red

B. green

C. yellow

6. What color is the car?

A. blue

B. yellow

C. red

7. Circle all of the blue shapes.

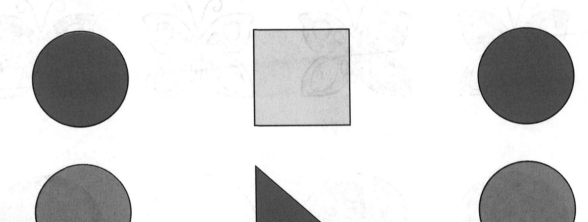

8. Circle the red triangle.

 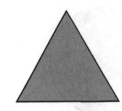 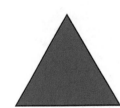 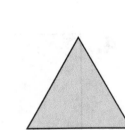

TRY IT

Compare Sizes

Compare Large and Small

Follow the directions for each problem.

1. Look at the purple triangle. Find all triangles that are the same size as that triangle. Color them purple.

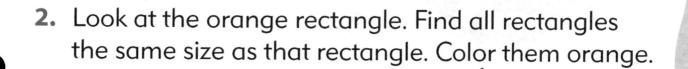

2. Look at the orange rectangle. Find all rectangles the same size as that rectangle. Color them orange.

3. Look at the squares. Color the small squares red and the large squares blue.

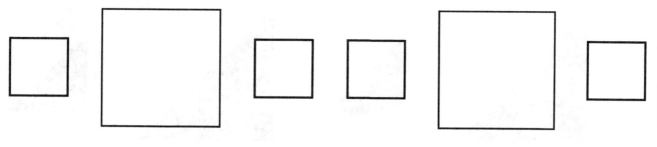

TRY IT

Read each problem and circle the answer.

4. Which object is large?

5. Which object is small?

6. Circle the large blue square.

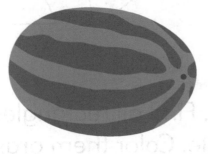

7. Circle the small triangles.

TRY IT

Sizes, Shapes, and Colors

Beary Large

Color the shapes in the picture as shown.

circles
yellow

rectangles
blue

triangles
green

squares
red

T R Y   I T

Read each problem and circle the answer.

1. What shape is shown here?

A. rectangle   B. circle   C. square

---

2. What shape is shown here?

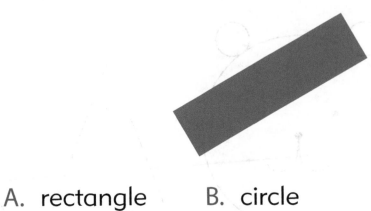

A. rectangle   B. circle   C. square

---

3. What shape is shown here?

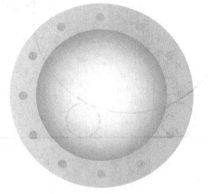

A. rectangle   B. circle   C. square

T R Y   I T

Sort by Color

Color Sort

1. Circle all of the yellow objects.

2. Circle all of the red objects.

3. Circle all of the green objects.

4. Circle all of the blue objects.

T R Y   I T

5. The grapes are purple. Circle all of the purple objects.

6. The cup is orange. Circle all of the orange objects.

7. The crayon is pink. Circle all of the pink objects.

Sort by Shape
Sort Shapes

Cut out each card.

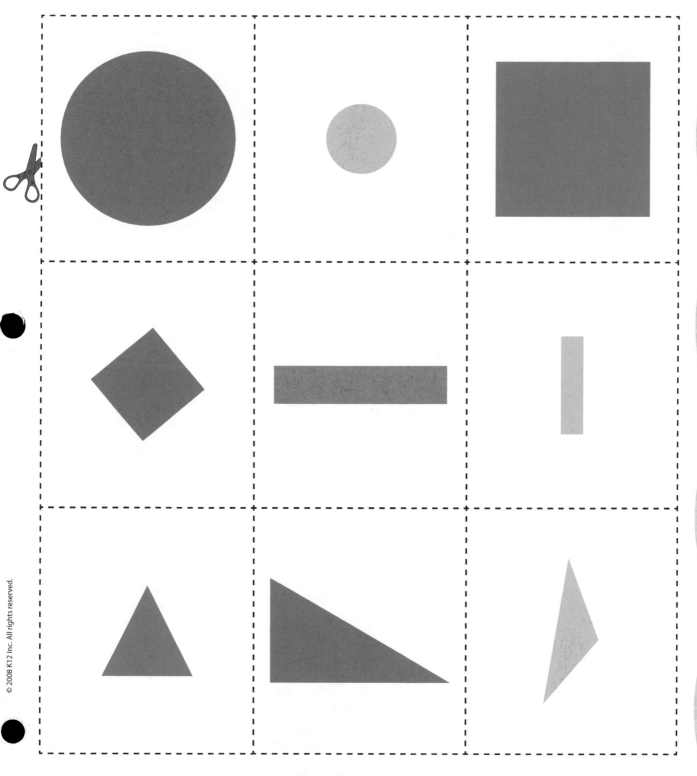

TRY IT

Sort by Size

Size Roundup

1. Circle all of the larger objects.

TRY IT

2. Color all of the shapes that are the same size.

3. Serena collects smaller things. Which of the following objects would **not** fit into her collection?

4. Circle all of the smaller fish.

TRY IT

Sort Different Ways

Different Groups

Choose how you want to sort the cut-out shapes.
Sort them into groups. Glue each group to a suitcase.
Then circle the sentence that tells how you sorted.

1. I sorted by color.

   I sorted by size.

   I sorted by shape.

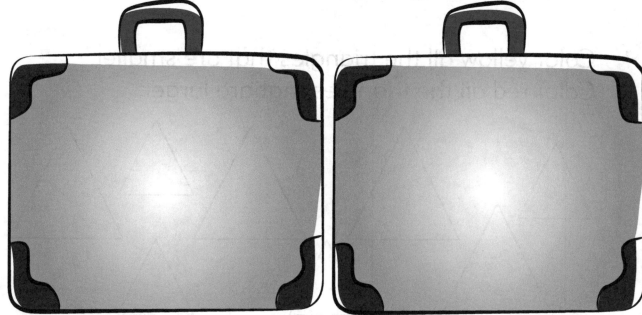

T R Y   I T

2. What is the same about each of these things?
Circle the answer.

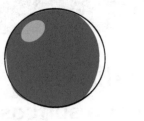   

They are all animals.   They are all green.

---

3. Serena loves to collect things. Here is her collection.

Which of these will fit into Serena's collection?
Circle it.

---

4. Color yellow all the triangles that are smaller.
Color red all the triangles that are larger.

TRY IT

Sort Different Ways

Different Groups

Cut out the shapes.

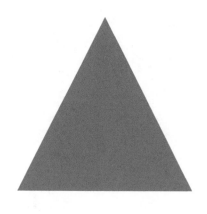

T R Y   I T

Name:

Color the shapes as shown.

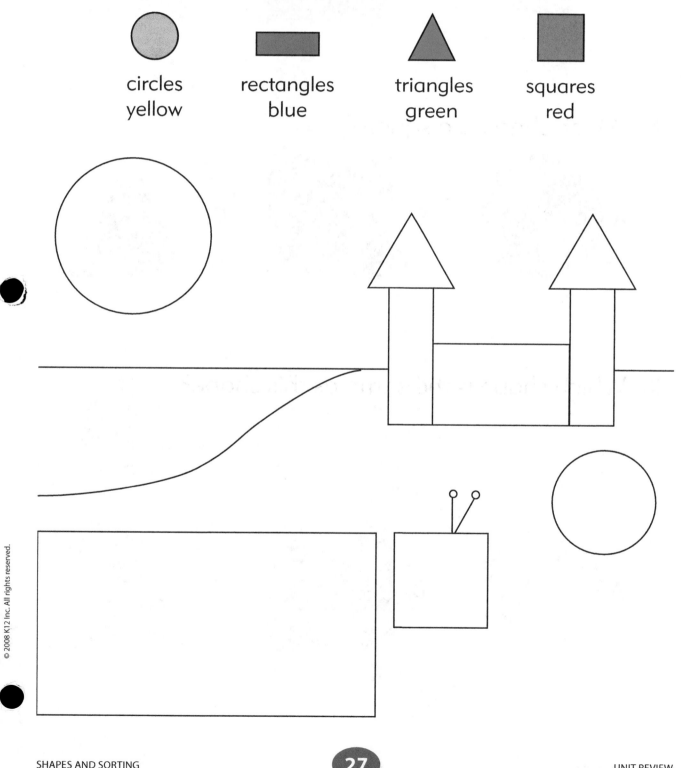

circles
yellow

rectangles
blue

triangles
green

squares
red

UNIT REVIEW

Read each problem and circle the answer.

1. Which shape is a triangle?

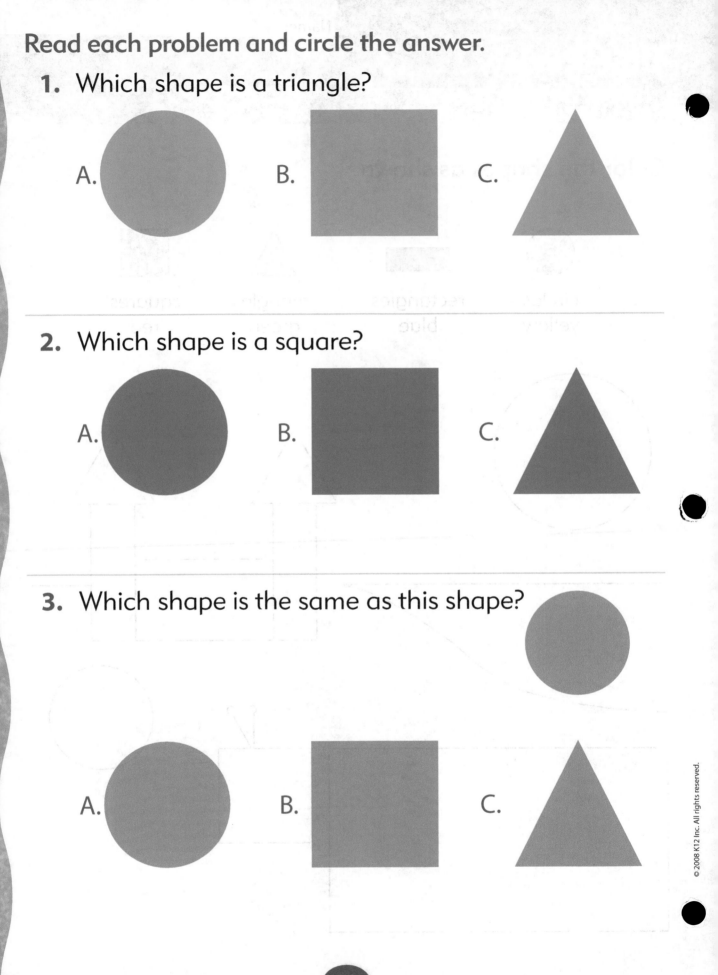

A.

B.

C.

2. Which shape is a square?

A.

B.

C.

3. Which shape is the same as this shape?

A.

B.

C.

4. Which object is smaller?

A.

B.

5. Which object is larger?

A.

B.

6. Look at the bird.
What color is the bird?

A. red

B. blue

C. yellow

7. Look at the clock.
What shape is the clock?

A. circle

B. square

C. triangle

Follow the directions for each problem.

8. Circle all the purple items.

9. Circle all the rectangles.

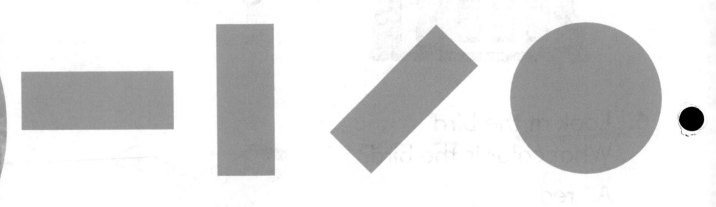

10. Color all the shapes that are the same size.

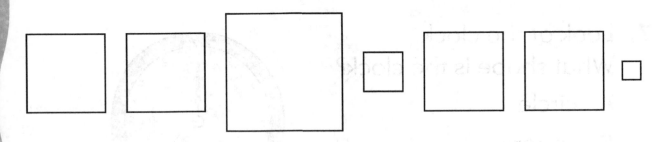

UNIT REVIEW

Which Object Is Different?

Does It Belong?

Look at the objects in each row. Circle the object that does **not** belong in the group, and tell why the object does not belong.

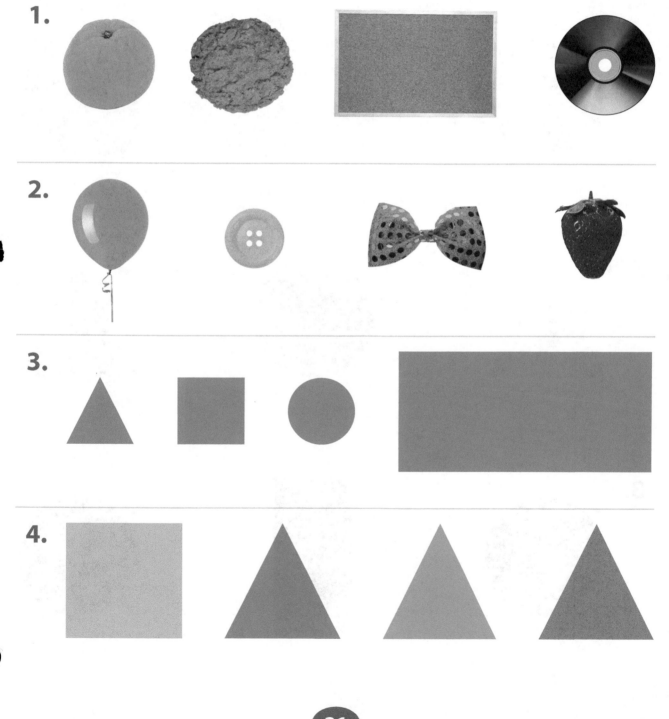

1.

2.

3.

4.

TRY IT

Circle the shape that does **not** belong in the group.

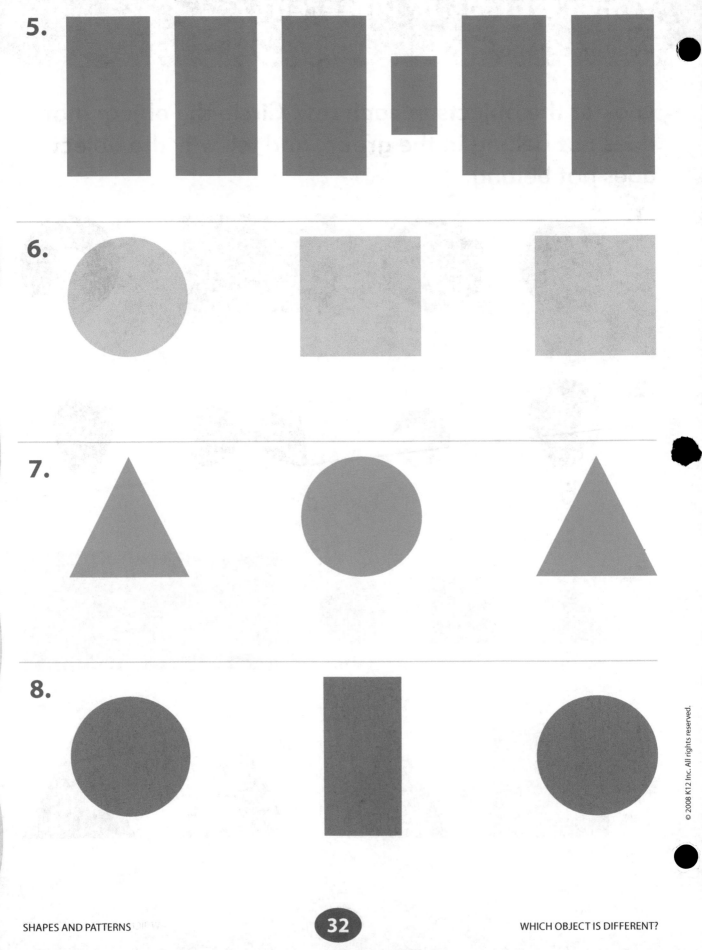

5.

6.

7.

8.

TRY IT

AB and ABB Patterns

Patterns Are Fun

Write A or B on each blank line to label each pattern.

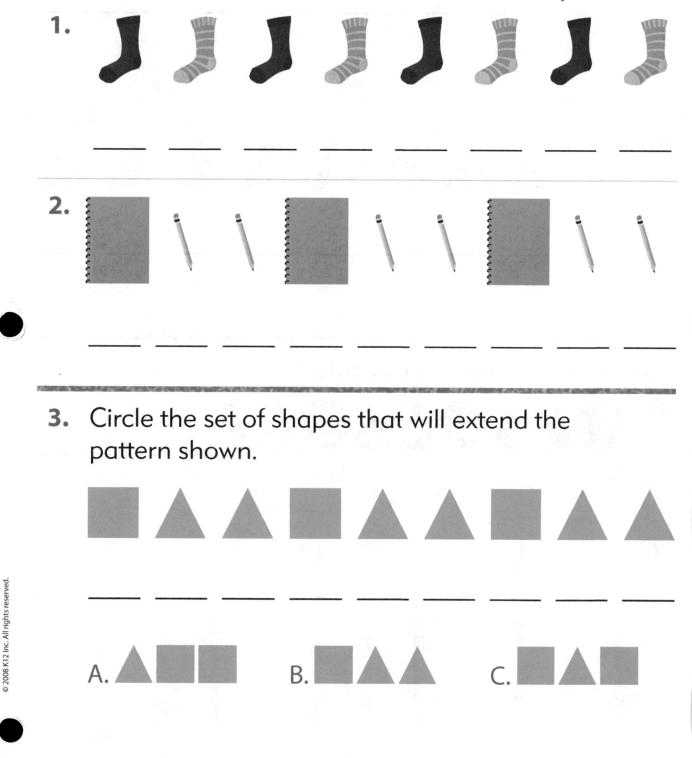

1.

_____ _____ _____ _____ _____ _____ _____ _____

2.

_____ _____ _____ _____ _____ _____ _____ _____ _____

3. Circle the set of shapes that will extend the pattern shown.

_____ _____ _____ _____ _____

A.   B.   C.

T R Y   I T

Write A or B on each blank line to label each pattern.

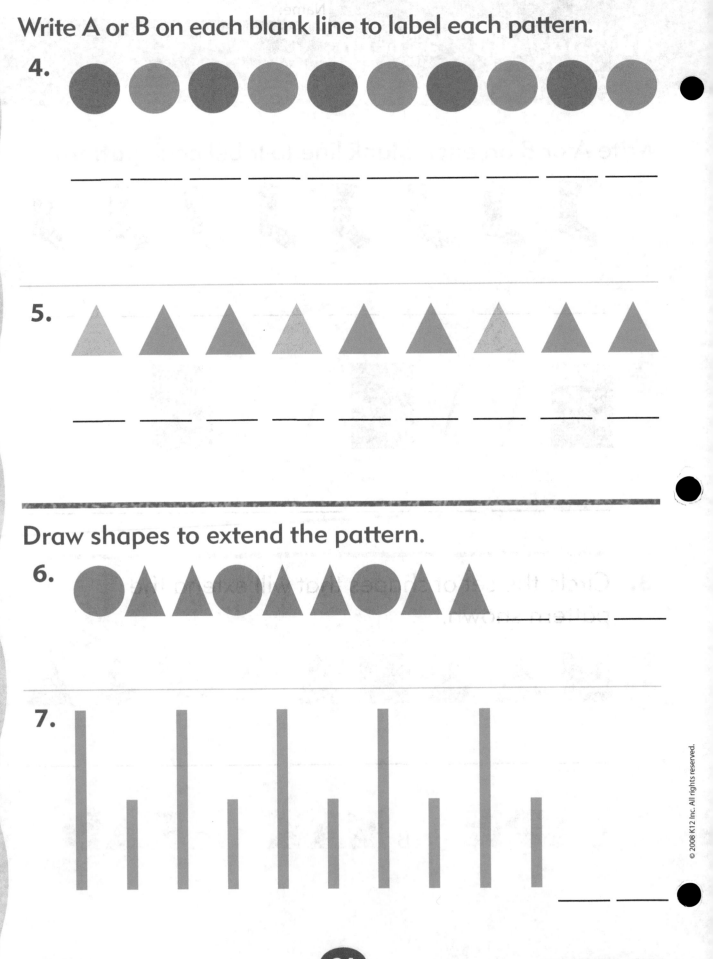

4.

____ ____ ____ ____ ____ ____ ____ ____ ____ ____

5.

____ ____ ____ ____ ____ ____ ____ ____

Draw shapes to extend the pattern.

6.

7.

TRY IT

AAAB and AAB Patterns

Baseball Patterns

Circle the core in each pattern. Then use the letters A and B to label each pattern on the blank lines below.

1.

___ ___ ___ ___ ___ ___ ___ ___ ___

2.

___ ___ ___ ___ ___ ___ ___ ___ ___ ___ ___ ___

Draw the next shapes in each pattern on the blank lines.

3.  ___ ___ ___ ___

4. ___ ___ ___

T R Y   I T

5. What is the rule for this pattern? Write it on the blank lines.

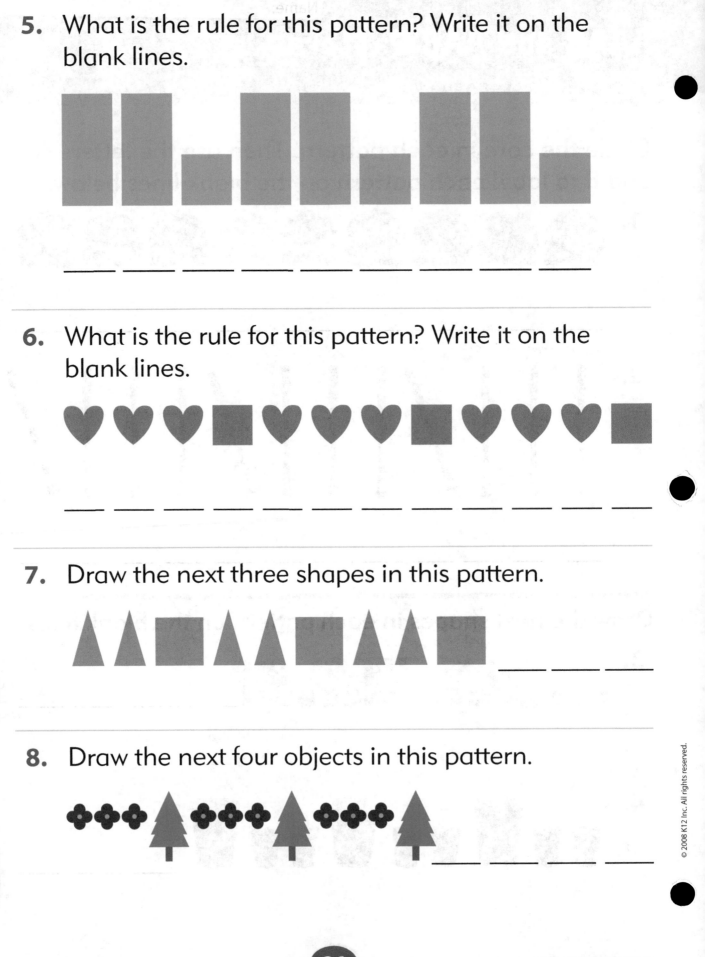

___ ___ ___ ___ ___ ___ ___ ___ ___

6. What is the rule for this pattern? Write it on the blank lines.

___ ___ ___ ___ ___ ___ ___ ___ ___ ___ ___ ___

7. Draw the next three shapes in this pattern.

___ ___ ___

8. Draw the next four objects in this pattern.

___ ___ ___ ___

TRY IT

ABCC and ABC Patterns

Kitchen Patterns

Circle the pattern shown with these bowls.

1.

ABCC   ABC

Circle the pattern shown with these glasses.

2.

ABCC   ABC

Circle the pattern shown with these mugs.

3.

ABCC   ABC

Draw pictures to extend each pattern.

4.

_____ _____ _____

5.

_____ _____ _____ _____

TRY IT

6. What is the pattern core for this pattern?

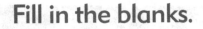

___ ___ ___ ___ ___ ___ ___ ___ ___

7. What is the pattern core for this pattern?

___ ___ ___ ___ ___ ___ ___

8. Draw the next two shapes in this pattern.

___ ___

9. Draw the next three shapes in this pattern.

___ ___

Circle the answer.

10. Which set of shapes is in an ABCC pattern?

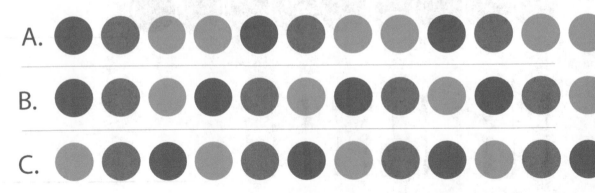

A.

B.

C.

TRY IT

Unit Review

Checkpoint Practice

Which shape is different? Follow the directions.

1. One shape is a different shape. Circle the shape that does **not** belong in the group.

2. One shape is a different size. Circle the shape that does **not** belong in the group.

3. Circle the shape that does **not** belong in the group.

4. Circle the shape that does **not** belong in the group.

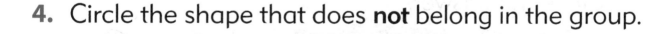

Follow the directions.

5. Label the pattern. Use the letters A and B.

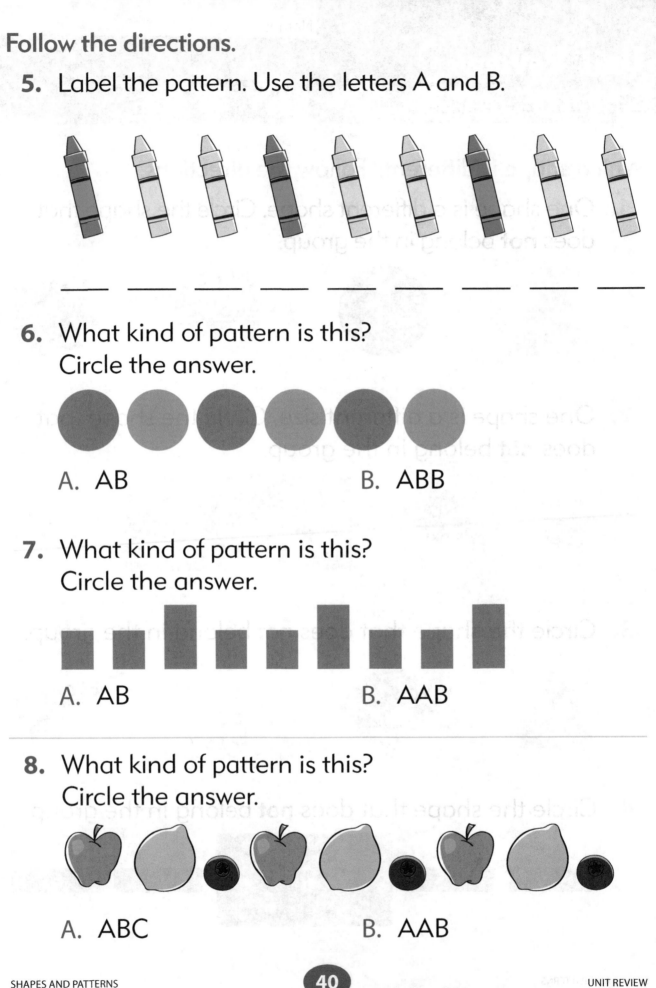

___ ___ ___ ___ ___ ___ ___ ___ ___

6. What kind of pattern is this?
Circle the answer.

A. AB   B. ABB

7. What kind of pattern is this?
Circle the answer.

A. AB   B. AAB

8. What kind of pattern is this?
Circle the answer.

A. ABC   B. AAB

UNIT REVIEW

Complete the pattern. Follow the directions.

9. Draw the next leaves in the pattern.

_____ _____ _____

10. Draw the next winter items in the pattern.

_____ _____ _____

11. Draw the next line in the pattern.

_____

12. Draw the next two shapes in the pattern.

_____ _____

13. Draw the next two shapes in the pattern.

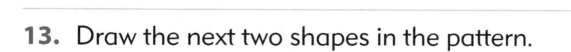

_____ _____

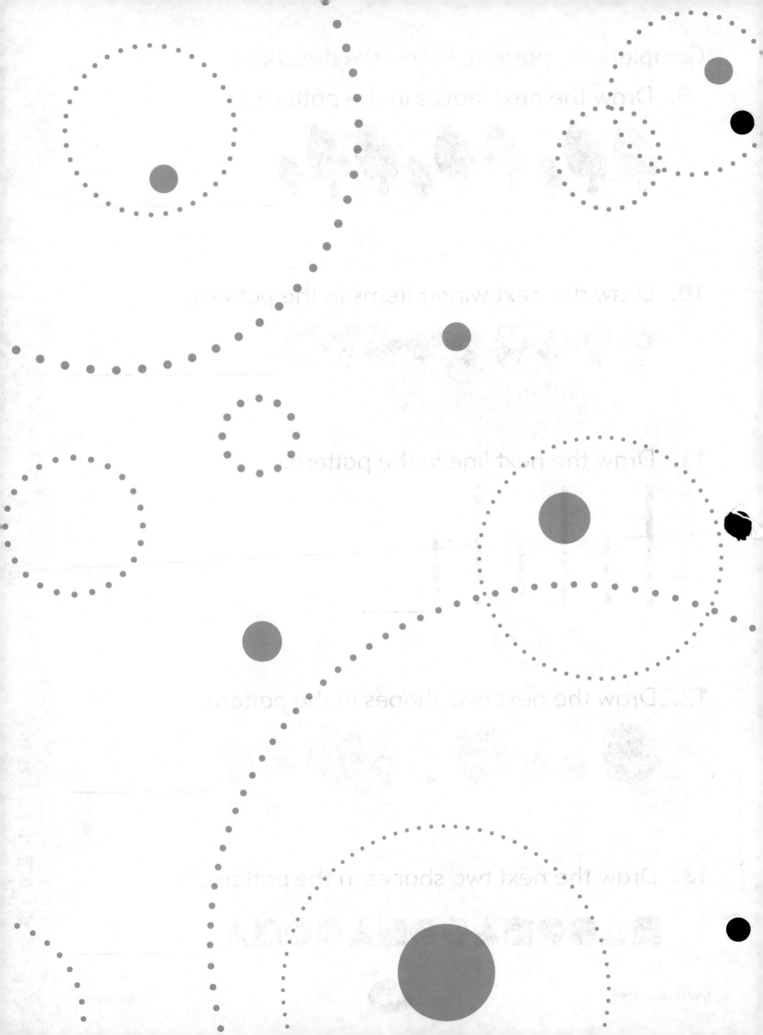

Name:

Circle the answer choice that shows the correct number.

1. 2 kittens

A.   B.   C.

2. 4 butterflies

A.   B.   C.

3. 5 fish

A.   B.   C.

Draw objects to show each number.

4. 4 trees

5. 2 people

TRY IT

Count the objects and say the number. Circle the answer.

6. How many stars?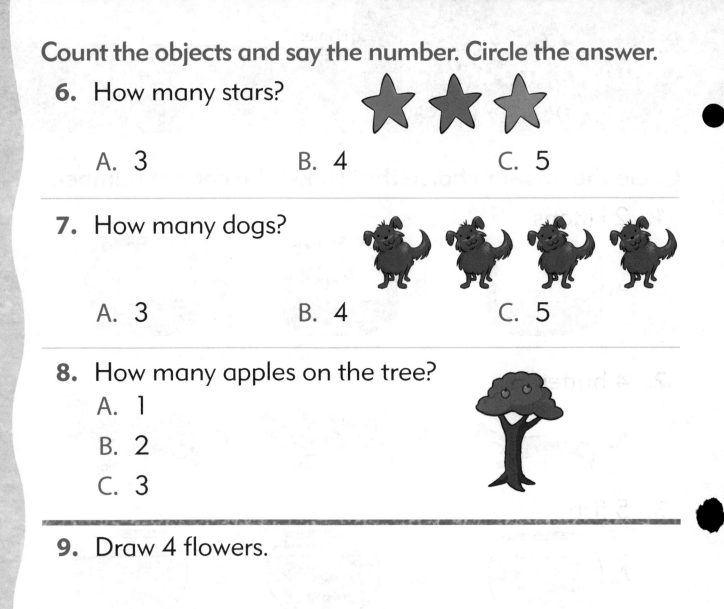

    A. 3   B. 4   C. 5

7. How many dogs?

    A. 3   B. 4   C. 5

8. How many apples on the tree?
    A. 1
    B. 2
    C. 3

9. Draw 4 flowers.

10. Draw 5 hearts.

11. Draw 2 clouds.

TRY IT

Count and Show 0 Through 5

Numbers 0 Through 5

Count the objects. Circle the number that tells how many objects you counted.

1. Count the teddy bears.

3   4   5

2. Count the blocks.

3   4   5

3. Count the apples on the plate.

0   1   2

4. Count the objects inside the basket.

0   1   2

Draw beans to show each number.

5. 4

6. 2

7. 0

8. 5

T R Y   I T

Count the objects. Circle the answer.

9. Count the balloons.

A. 1

B. 2

C. 3

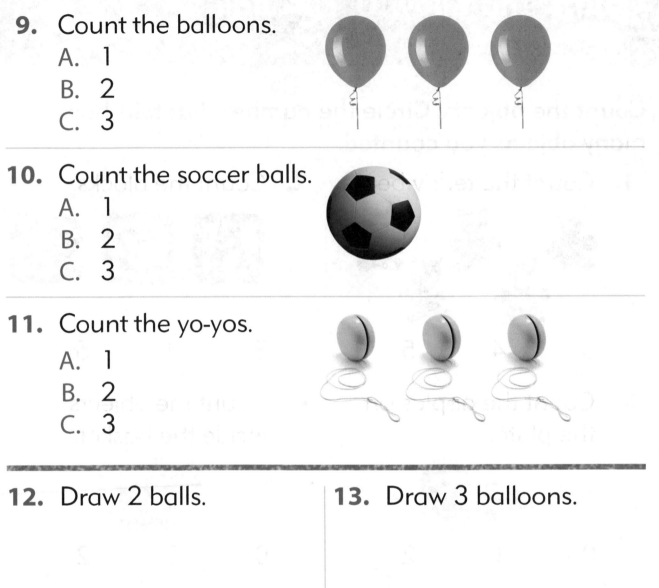

10. Count the soccer balls.

A. 1

B. 2

C. 3

11. Count the yo-yos.

A. 1

B. 2

C. 3

12. Draw 2 balls.

13. Draw 3 balloons.

14. Draw 5 yo-yos.

TRY IT

Write Numerals Through 5

Count and Write Numerals

For each problem, count the objects.
Then write the number.

1.

_____

2.

_____

3.

_____

4.

_____

5.

_____

L E A R N

Count the fish in the bowl. Write the number.

6.

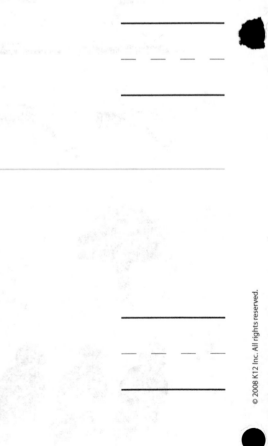

_____

_ _ _ _ _ _ _

_____

7.

_____

_ _ _ _ _ _ _

_____

8.

_____

_ _ _ _ _ _ _

_____

Write Numerals Through 5

Count and Write 0 Through 5

Look at the picture and write the number for the objects you are counting.

1. Count the trees.

    _____

    _ _ _ _ _

    _____

2. Count the birds.

    _____

    _ _ _ _ _

    _____

3. Count the clouds.

    _____

    _ _ _ _ _

    _____

4. Count the flowers.

    _____

    _ _ _ _ _

    _____

5. Count the suns.

    _____

    _ _ _ _ _

    _____

6. Count the bunnies.

    _____

    _ _ _ _ _

    _____

T R Y   I T

Read each problem, and then write the number.

7. Write the number zero.

_____
- - - - -
_____

8. Write the number one.

_____
- - - - -
_____

9. Write the number two.

_____
- - - - -
_____

10. Write the number three.

_____
- - - - -
_____

11. Write the number four.

_____
- - - - -
_____

12. Write the number five.

_____
- - - - -
_____

Sides of a Shape
Count the Sides

Cut out the shapes.

LEARN

Sides of a Shape

How Many Sides?

For Problems 1–2, circle the shape that has the same number of sides as the shape shown above the answer choices.

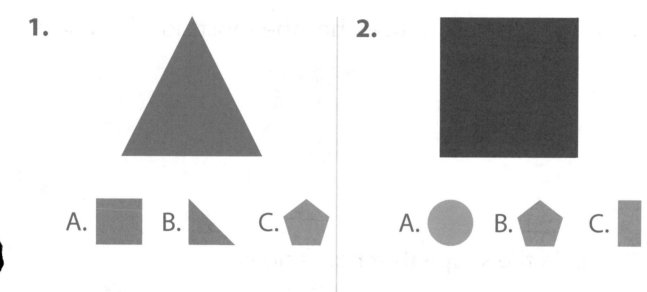

1.   A.   B.   C.

2.   A.   B.   C.

For Problems 3–4, circle the shape that has the most sides.

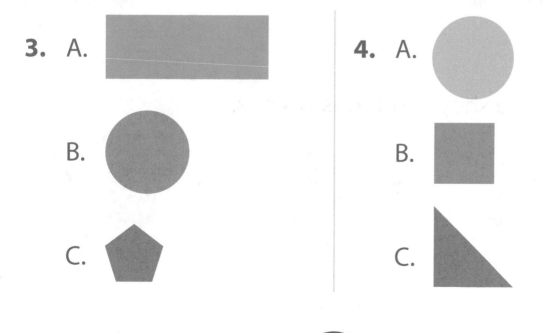

3. A.

B.

C.

4. A.

B.

C.

TRY IT

5. Which of these shapes has the most sides? Circle it.

A. 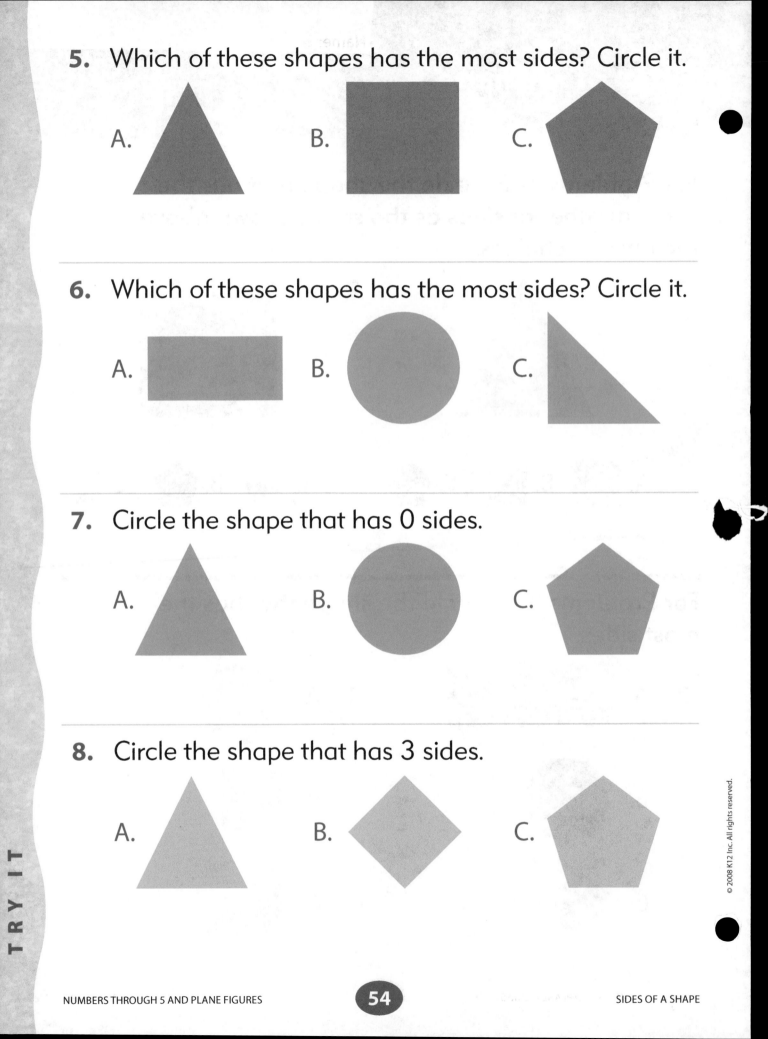 B. C.

6. Which of these shapes has the most sides? Circle it.

A. B. C.

7. Circle the shape that has 0 sides.

A. B. C.

8. Circle the shape that has 3 sides.

A. B. C.

TRY IT

Corners of a Shape

Shape Poster

Cut out the shapes.

L E A R N

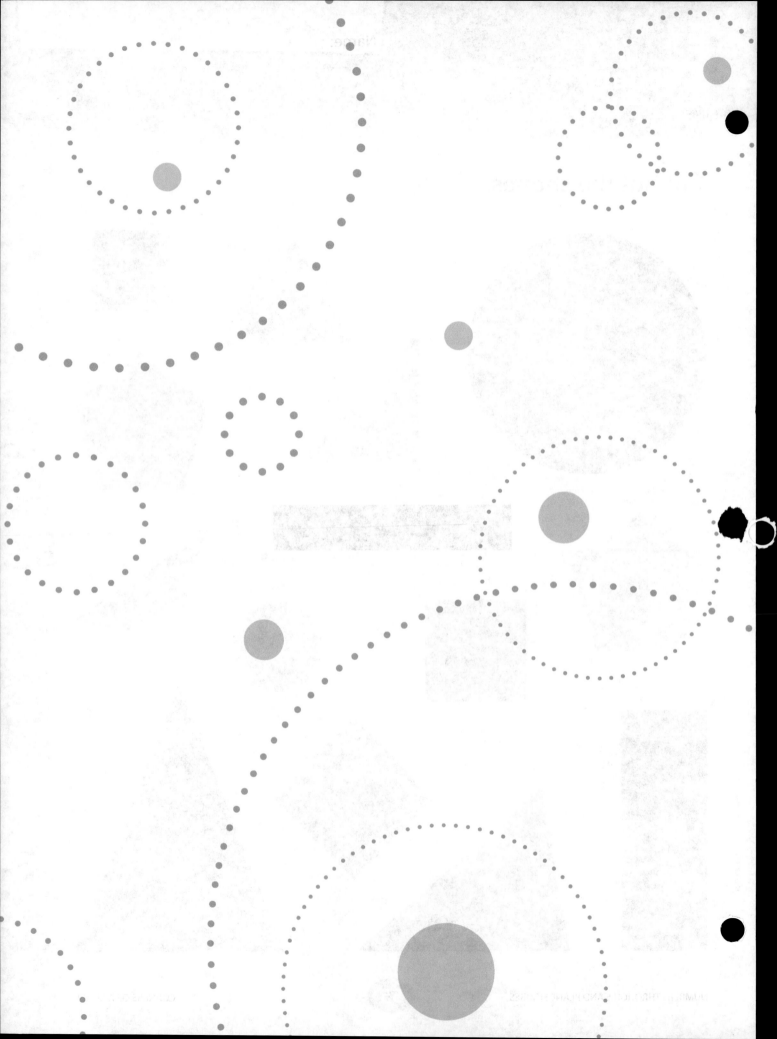

Name:

For Problems 1–2, circle the shape that has the same number of corners as the shape shown.

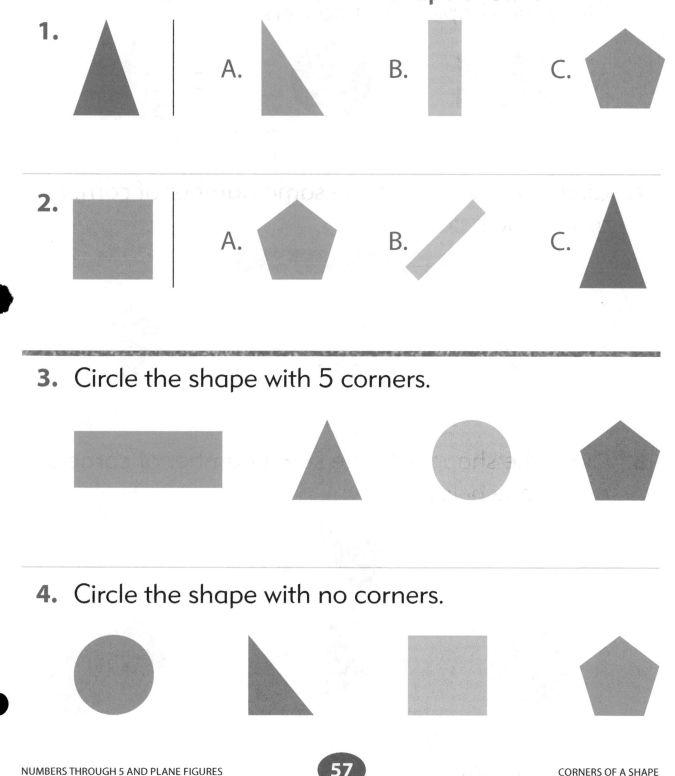

1.

A.   B.   C.

2.

A.   B.   C.

3. Circle the shape with 5 corners.

4. Circle the shape with no corners.

T R Y   I T

5. Circle the shape with no corners.

A. B. C.

6. Circle the shape with 4 corners.

A. B. C.

7. Circle the shape with the same number of corners as the one below.

A. B. C.

8. Circle the shape with the same number of corners as the one below.

A. B. C.

TRY IT

Sides and Corners of Shapes

Write Numerals 0 Through 5

Write the numbers 0, 1, 2, 3, 4, and 5.

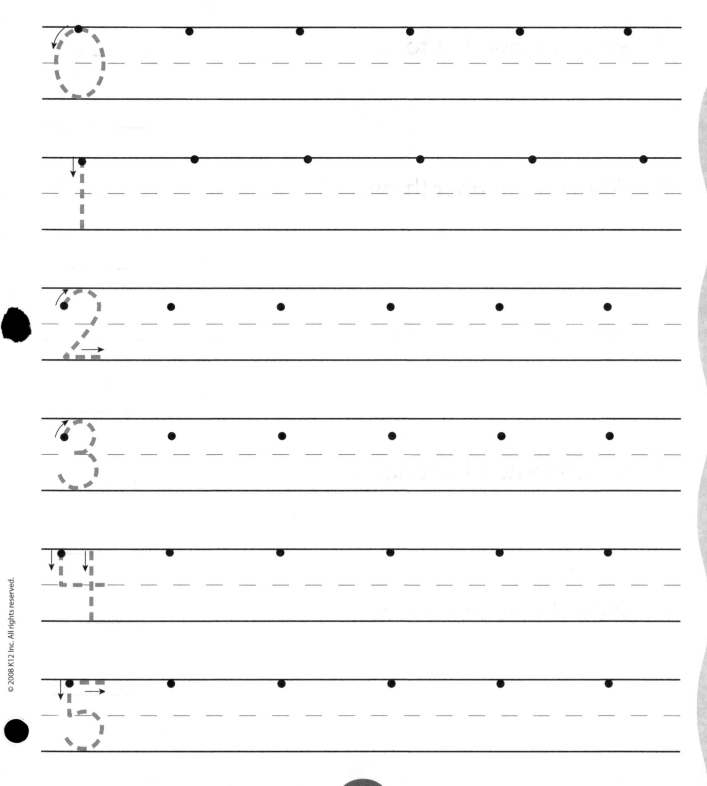

T R Y   I T

Read each problem, and then write the number.

1. Write the number five.   _____

2. Write the number four.   _____

3. Write the number three.   _____

4. Write the number two.   _____

5. Write the number one.   _____

6. Write the number zero.   _____

Unit Review

Checkpoint Practice

Count the objects. Circle the number that you counted.

1. How many sheep are on the hill?

A. 3   B. 4   C. 5

2. How many pigs are in the mud?

A. 3   B. 4   C. 5

3. How many suns are there?

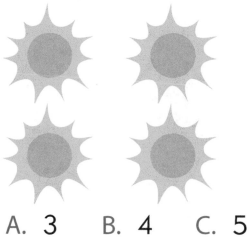

A. 3   B. 4   C. 5

4. How many roosters are there?

A. 4   B. 3   C. 2

UNIT REVIEW

Draw the number of objects.

5. Draw 4 eggs.

---

6. Draw 2 clouds.

---

7. Draw 3 sticks.

---

8. Draw 2 trees.

Write the number to complete each problem.

9. Write the number two.

‾‾‾‾‾‾‾‾‾‾‾

- - - - - - - - - -

‾‾‾‾‾‾‾‾‾‾‾

10. Write the number five.

‾‾‾‾‾‾‾‾‾‾‾

- - - - - - - - - -

‾‾‾‾‾‾‾‾‾‾‾

11. Write the number of cows inside the fence.

‾‾‾‾‾‾‾‾‾‾‾

- - - - - - - - - -

‾‾‾‾‾‾‾‾‾‾‾

12. Write the number of cows inside the fence.

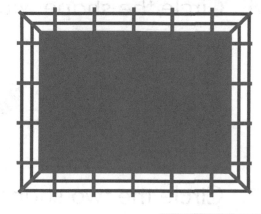

‾‾‾‾‾‾‾‾‾‾‾

- - - - - - - - - -

‾‾‾‾‾‾‾‾‾‾‾

13. Count the tractors. Write the number.

‾‾‾‾‾‾‾‾‾‾‾

- - - - - - - - - -

‾‾‾‾‾‾‾‾‾‾‾

14. Count the barns. Write the number.

‾‾‾‾‾‾‾‾‾‾‾

- - - - - - - - - -

‾‾‾‾‾‾‾‾‾‾‾

Follow the directions about counting sides and corners.

15. Circle the shape that has the same number of sides as the red square shown on the left.

16. Circle the shape with 0 corners.

17. Circle the two shapes that have the same number of sides.

18. Circle the two shapes that have the same number of corners.

19. Which of these shapes has the most sides? Circle it.

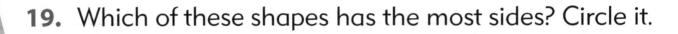

Count Through 10
Count Fruit

Count aloud the fruit on each plate.

1. Blueberries

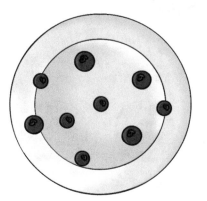

2. Strawberries

3. Oranges

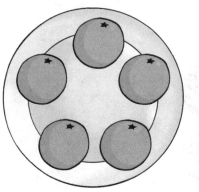

4. Grapes

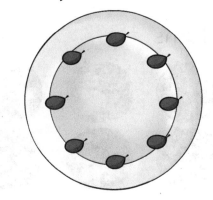

5. Raspberries

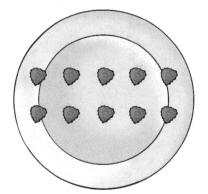

6. Bananas

T R Y I T

Count aloud the fruit in each group.

7. Apples

8. Peaches

9. Plums

10. Lemons

TRY IT

Show an Amount Through 10

Show an Amount

Use blocks to show each amount.

1. 8

2. 6

3. 10

4. 0

5. 7

6. 9

TRY IT

Draw the objects to show each amount.

7. 6 dots

8. 10 dots

9. 7 squares

10. 9 circles

Draw objects of your choice to show each amount.

11. 8 objects

12. 5 objects

TRY IT

Represent Amounts

Show the Amount

Read each problem. Place blocks or draw in the large squares and circles.

1. Draw 8 circles.

2. Draw 10 lines.

3. Show 7 cubes.

4. Show 0 cubes.

TRY IT

Place blocks or draw in the space below each problem.

5. Draw 8 dots.

6. Draw 5 dots.

7. Show 7 circle blocks.

8. Show 9 circle blocks.

TRY IT

Count Aloud Through 10

Numbers Through 10

Count aloud the objects on the rug. Circle the number that tells how many.

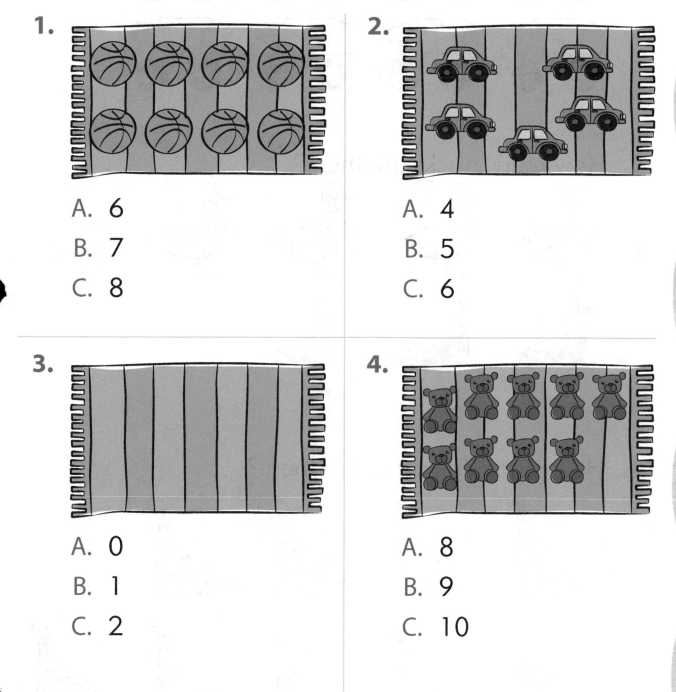

1.

A. 6

B. 7

C. 8

2.

A. 4

B. 5

C. 6

3.

A. 0

B. 1

C. 2

4.

A. 8

B. 9

C. 10

TRY IT

Count aloud the toys in the group.
Then say the number that tells how many.

5. How many toy trucks are there?

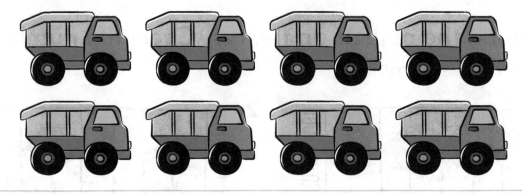

6. How many ducks are there?

7. How many dinosaurs are there?

TRY IT

Name:

Show Amounts in Different Ways

Represent the Amount

Draw the correct number of objects in the box.

1. Draw 9 triangles in the box.

2. Draw 6 triangles in the box.

3. Draw 5 dots in the box.

TRY IT

Place the correct number of blocks in the box.

4. Place 8 blocks in the box.

5. Place 4 blocks in the box.

6. Place 3 blocks in the box.

TRY IT

Write Numerals 1 Through 10

Know Your Numerals Through 10

Look at the picture. Write the answer to each problem.

1. Count the apples. Write the number. _____

2. Count the chairs. Write the number. _____

3. Count the empty plates.
   Write the number. _____

4. Count the vases. Write the number. _____

5. Count the flowers. Write the number. _____

T R Y   I T

Read each problem and write the answer.

6. Write the number zero.

_____
- - - - -
_____

7. Write the number nine.

_____
- - - - -
_____

8. Write the number two.

_____
- - - - -
_____

9. Write the number five.

_____

_____

10. Write the number six.

_____

_____

TRY IT

More, Fewer, and Equal

Count and Compare

Read each problem and follow the directions.

1. Circle the group with more kittens.

2. Circle the group with fewer balls of yarn.

3. Color the groups that have equal numbers of dog bones.

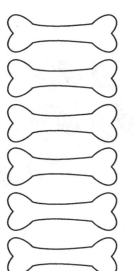 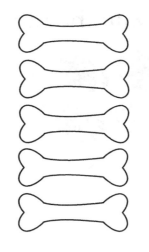 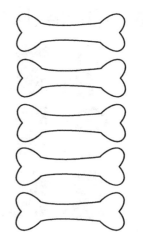

LEARN

4. Circle the group with the fewest bees.

5. Color the groups that have equal numbers of leaves.

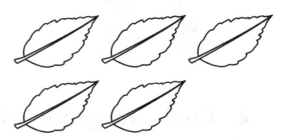

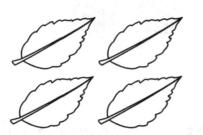

6. Circle the group with the most shoes.

More, Fewer, and Equal

Compare Objects in Groups

Read the problems and follow the directions.

1. Circle the group with more cars.

2. Circle the group with fewer cubes.

3. Circle the group with the most bananas.

4. Circle the group with fewer stars.

TRY IT

5. Circle the group with more boats.

6. Sue has 3 balls, Lucy has 9 balls, and Jeff has 3 balls. Circle the 2 children who have the same number of balls.

7. Tim has 8 cookies, Sally has 3 cookies, and Bob has 8 cookies. Circle the 2 children who have equal numbers of cookies.

TRY IT

Compare and Order Groups

More, Fewer, Most, and Least

Circle the answer.

1. Which group has more cubes?

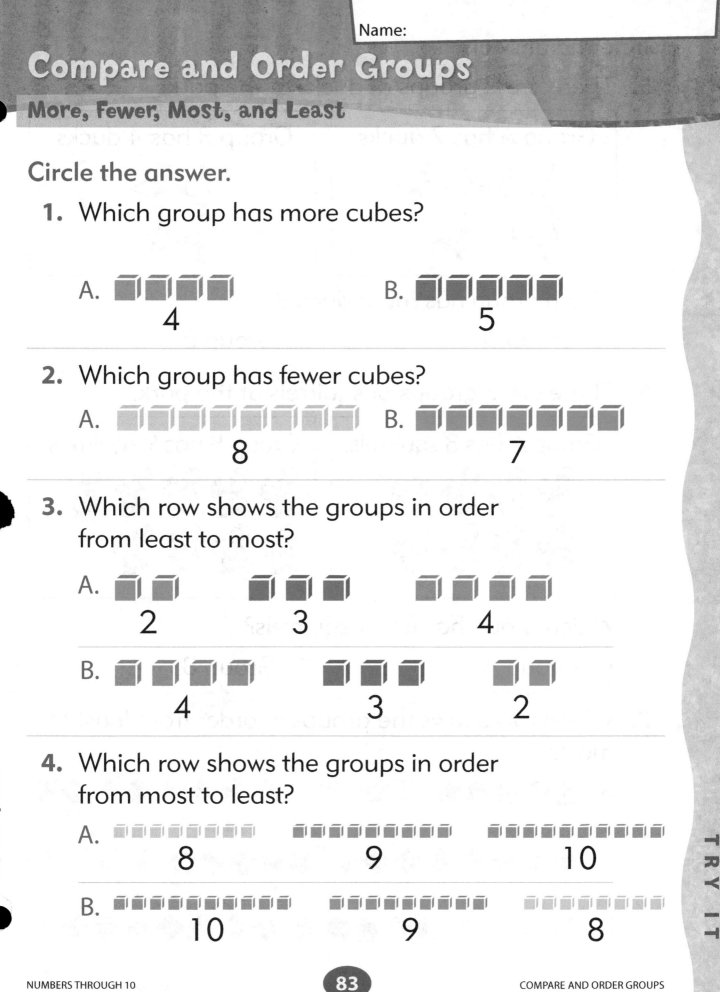

A.   4

B.   5

2. Which group has fewer cubes?

A.   8

B.   7

3. Which row shows the groups in order from least to most?

A.   2   3   4

B.   4   3   2

4. Which row shows the groups in order from most to least?

A.   8   9   10

B.   10   9   8

TRY IT

Circle the answer.

5. There are 2 groups of ducks at the park.

 Group A has 7 ducks.

 Group B has 4 ducks.

Which group has more ducks?

A. Group A   B. Group B

6. There are 2 groups of squirrels at the park.

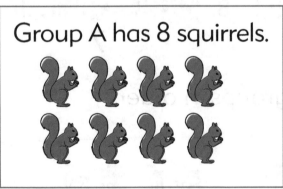 Group A has 8 squirrels.

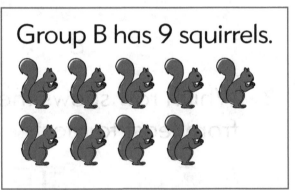 Group B has 9 squirrels.

Which group has fewer squirrels?

A. Group A   B. Group B

7. Which row shows the groups in order from least to most?

TRY IT

Describe and Order Groups by Number

Describe and Order Groups

Circle the group with more objects.

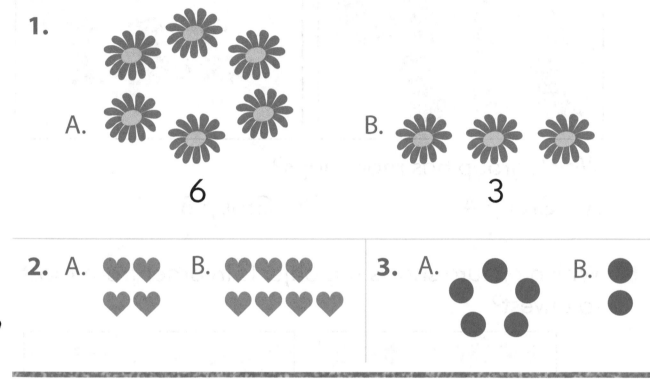

1.

A.

6

B.

3

2. A. B.

3. A. B.

---

4. Circle the row that shows the groups in order from fewest to most objects.

A.

B.

TRY IT

Read each problem. Circle the answer.

5. There are 2 groups of dogs.

Which group has more dogs?

A. Group A   B. Group B

6. Which picture shows the objects in order from most to fewest?

A.

B.

7. Which picture shows the objects in order from fewest to most?

A.

B.

TRY IT

Name:

Write Numbers to Describe Groups

Write Numbers 1-10

Place a block on each object. Write the number to show how many objects are in the group.

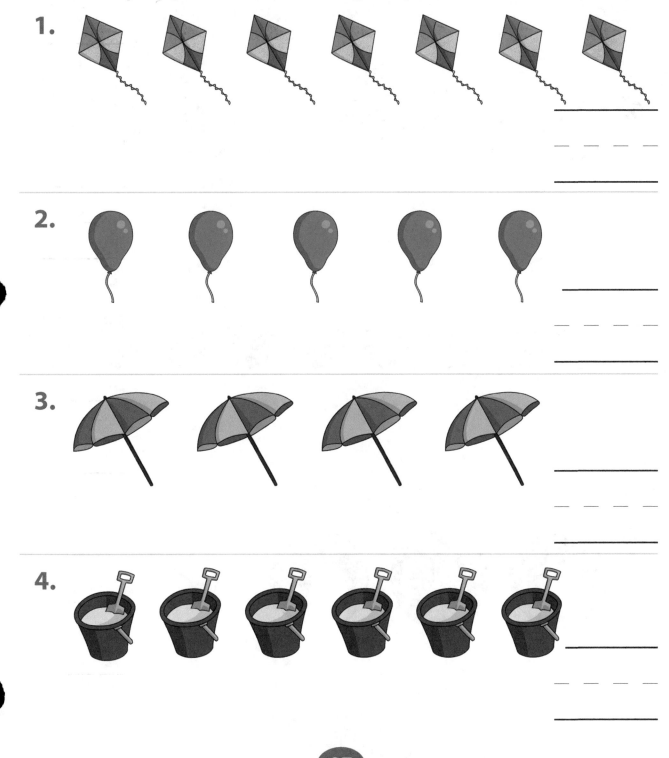

1. _____

2. _____

3. _____

4. _____

L E A R N

Write the number to show how many objects are in the group.

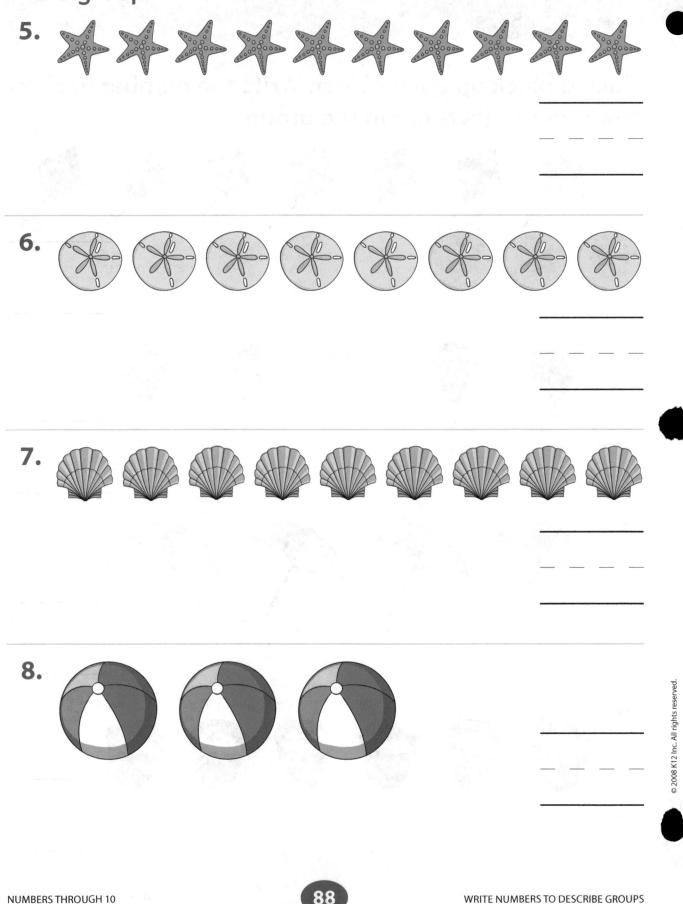

5.

_____
_ _ _ _ _
_____

6.

_____
_ _ _ _ _
_____

7.

_____
_ _ _ _ _
_____

8.

_____
_ _ _ _ _
_____

LEARN

Write Numbers to Describe Groups

Write How Many: Part 1

Write the number to show how many animals.

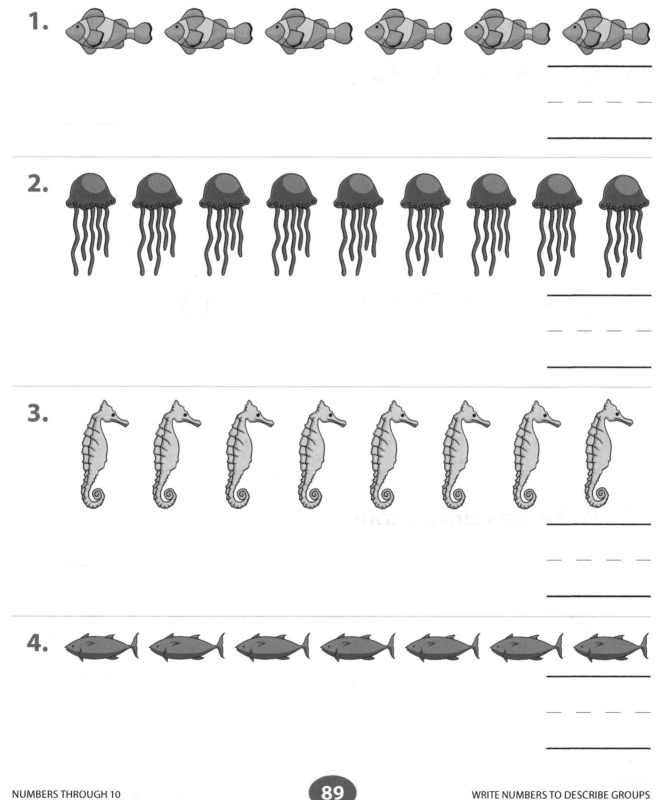

1.

2.

3.

4.

TRY IT

5. Write the number nine.

_____
- - - -
_____

6. Write the number two.

_____
- - - -
_____

7. Write the number ten.

_____
- - - -
_____

8. Write the number four.

_____
- - - -
_____

TRY IT

Write Numbers to Describe Groups

Write How Many: Part 2

Write the number to show how many in each group.
Then circle the group with more animals.

1.

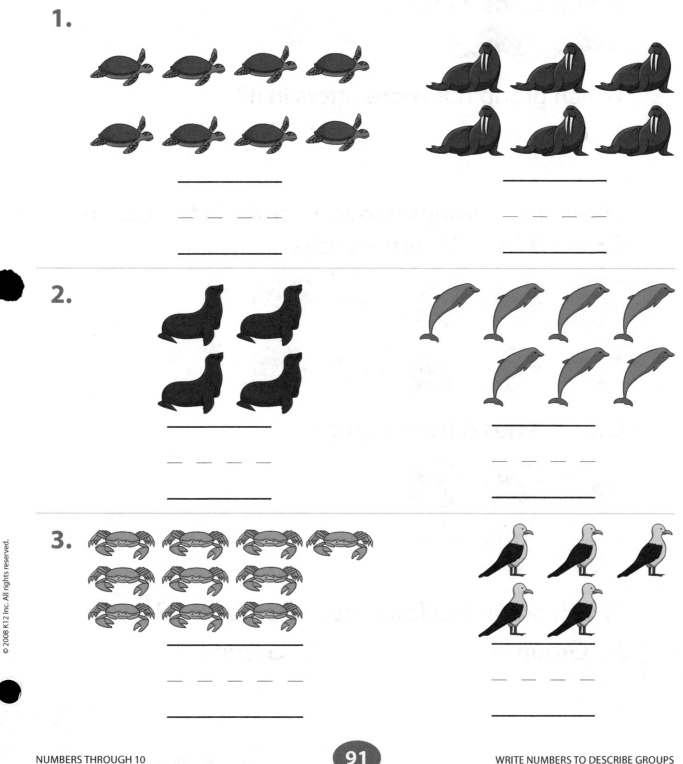

2.

3.

T R Y   I T

Read each problem. Circle the answer.

4. There are 2 groups of otters in the ocean.
Group A has 7 otters.

Group B has 2 otters.

Which group has more otters in it?

A. Group A

B. Group B

---

5. There are 2 groups of hermit crabs in the ocean.
Group A has 10 hermit crabs.

Group B has 6 hermit crabs.

Which group has fewer hermit crabs in it?

A. Group A

B. Group B

TRY IT

Name: _____

Read each problem and follow the directions.

1. Draw 9 dots in the box.

2. Write the number that tells how many triangles.

_____

- - - - -

_____

3. Circle the groups that have an equal number of stars.

4. Write the number of animals in each group. Then circle the group that has more animals.

_____

- - - - -

_____

_____

- - - - -

_____

UNIT REVIEW

Read each problem and follow the directions.

5. Circle the group that has more planes.

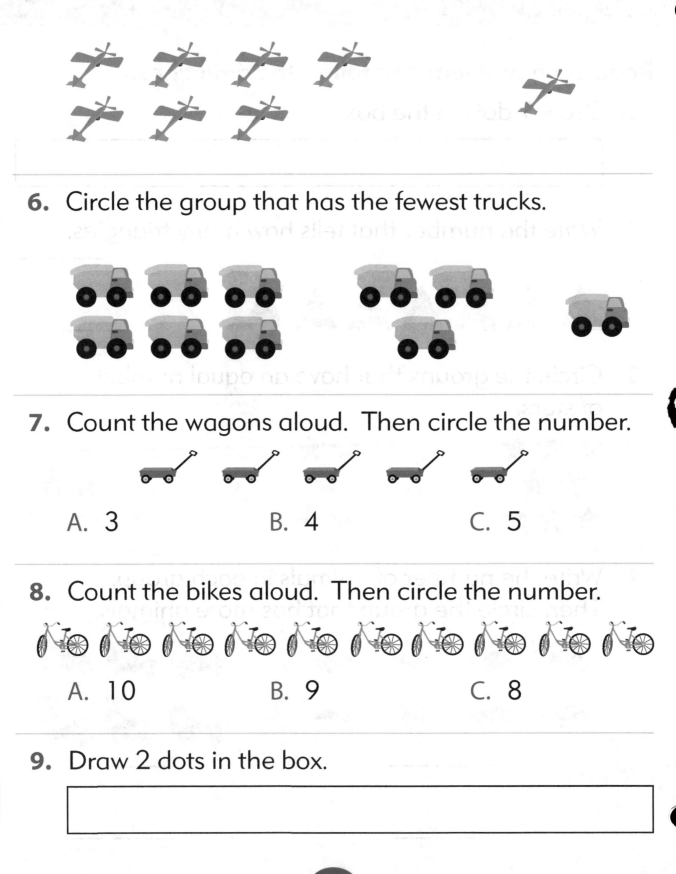

6. Circle the group that has the fewest trucks.

7. Count the wagons aloud. Then circle the number.

A. 3   B. 4   C. 5

8. Count the bikes aloud. Then circle the number.

A. 10   B. 9   C. 8

9. Draw 2 dots in the box.

10. Write the number eight.

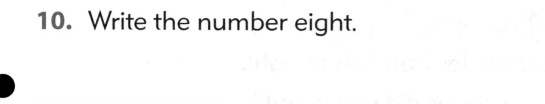

11. Circle the row with groups of objects that are ordered from least to most.

A. ●●● ▲▲▲▲▲ ■

B. ■ ●●● ▲▲▲▲▲

C. ▲▲▲▲▲ ●●● ■

12. Circle the row with groups of objects that are ordered from most to least.

A. ●●● ▲▲▲▲▲ ■

B. ■ ●●● ▲▲▲▲▲

C. ▲▲▲▲▲ ●●● ■

13. ■■■■■■■■

Count the squares from left to right.

How many squares did you count? _____

Count the squares from right to left.

How many squares did you count? _____

Did changing the direction you counted change the number of squares? Circle Yes or No.

A. Yes   B. No

14. ●●●●●●●●

Count the circles from left to right.

How many circles did you count? _____

Count the circles from right to left.

How many circles did you count? _____

Did changing the direction you counted change the number of circles? Choose Yes or No.

A. Yes   B. No

15. There are 2 groups of cars.

Group A has 3 cars.   Group B has 8 cars.

Which group has more cars? Circle the answer.

A. Group A   B. Group B

16. There are 2 groups of roller skates.

| Group A has 3 roller skates. | Group B has 4 roller skates. |

Which group has fewer skates? Circle the answer.

A. Group A   B. Group B

UNIT REVIEW

Unit Review

Use the May calendar to answer the problems.

1. Circle the name of the month.

2. Look for Wednesday at the top of the calendar. Color the box for Wednesday green.

3. Color the second day of May purple.

4. If today is May 12, what is tomorrow? Color the box for that day yellow.

❈ May ❈

Sunday	Monday	Tuesday	Wednesday	Thursday	Friday	Saturday
				1	2	3
4	5	6	7	8	9	10
11	12	13	14	15	16	17
18	19	20	21	22	23	24
25	26	27	28	29	30	31

Use the calendar to answer the problems.
Circle the answer.

May

Sunday	Monday	Tuesday	Wednesday	Thursday	Friday	Saturday
				1	2	3

5. Which day comes right after Monday?

    A. Sunday   B. Tuesday   C. Wednesday

6. Which day comes right before Tuesday?

    A. Thursday   B. Saturday   C. Monday

7. If today is Tuesday, what day is tomorrow?

    A. Monday   B. Wednesday   C. Friday

8. If yesterday was Tuesday, what day is today?

    A. Monday   B. Wednesday   C. Thursday

9. Which can a calendar measure?

    A. hours   B. minutes   C. days

UNIT REVIEW

Read each problem and circle the answer.

10. Which tool can measure days?

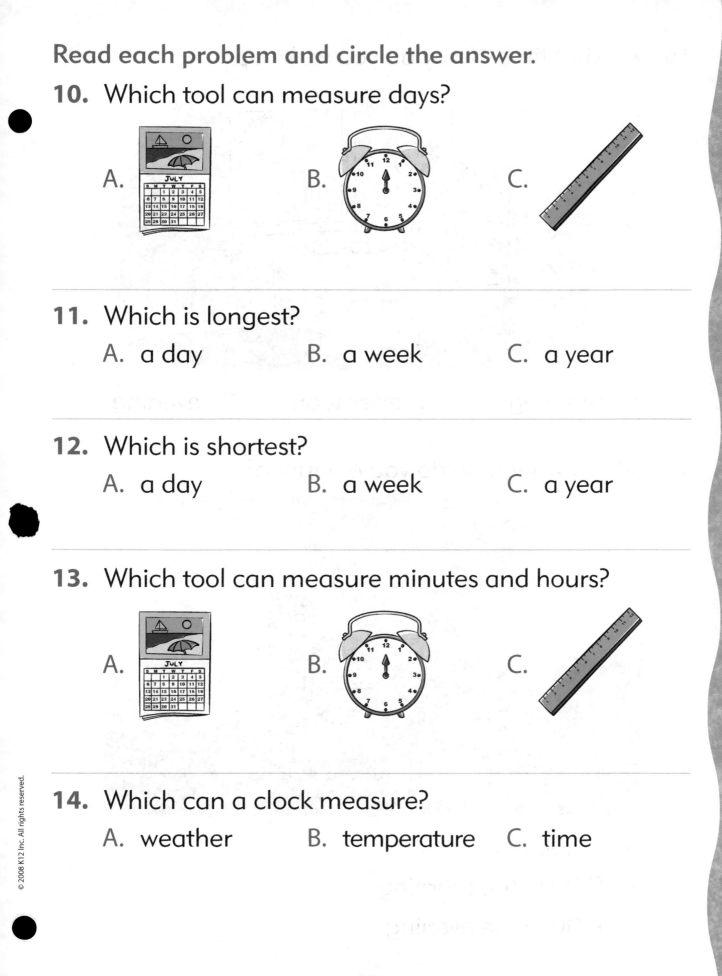

A.   B.   C.

11. Which is longest?

A. a day   B. a week   C. a year

12. Which is shortest?

A. a day   B. a week   C. a year

13. Which tool can measure minutes and hours?

A.   B.   C.

14. Which can a clock measure?

A. weather   B. temperature   C. time

15. At what time of day do you wake up?

A. morning   B. afternoon   C. evening

16. About what time do you eat lunch?

A. 12:00 noon

B. 9:00 in the morning

C. 6:00 in the evening

Collect Data and Pose Questions

Read each problem and follow the directions.

1. Count the spoons and forks. Write the results with numbers and pictures.

   _____spoons   _____ forks

2. Count the red, blue, and yellow bowls. Write the results with numbers.

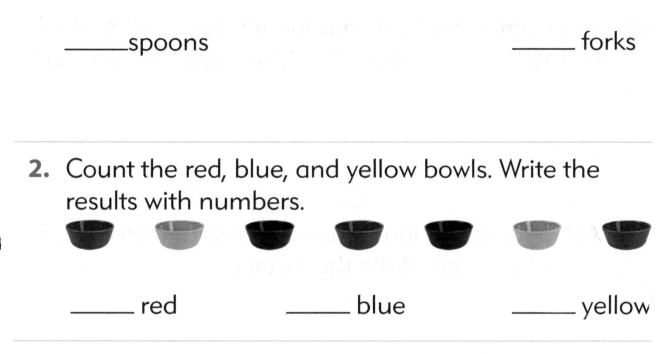

   _____ red   _____ blue   _____ yellow

3. You want to find out what meal your friends like best. What question should you ask? Say it aloud.

4. You want to find out what canned foods your family eats most. What question should you ask? Say it aloud.

T R Y   I T

Read each problem and follow the directions.

5. You want to find out your friends' favorite fruit. What question should you ask? Say it aloud.

6. You want to find out your friends' favorite baseball teams. What question should you ask? Say it aloud.

7. Ask 5 friends or family members what they ate for breakfast today. Write the results.

8. Ask 5 friends or family members what their favorite color is. Write the results.

TRY IT

Ways to Show Data

Color Tile Picture Graph

Use your color tiles to complete the picture graph.

Color Tiles

Each picture in the boxes equals 1.

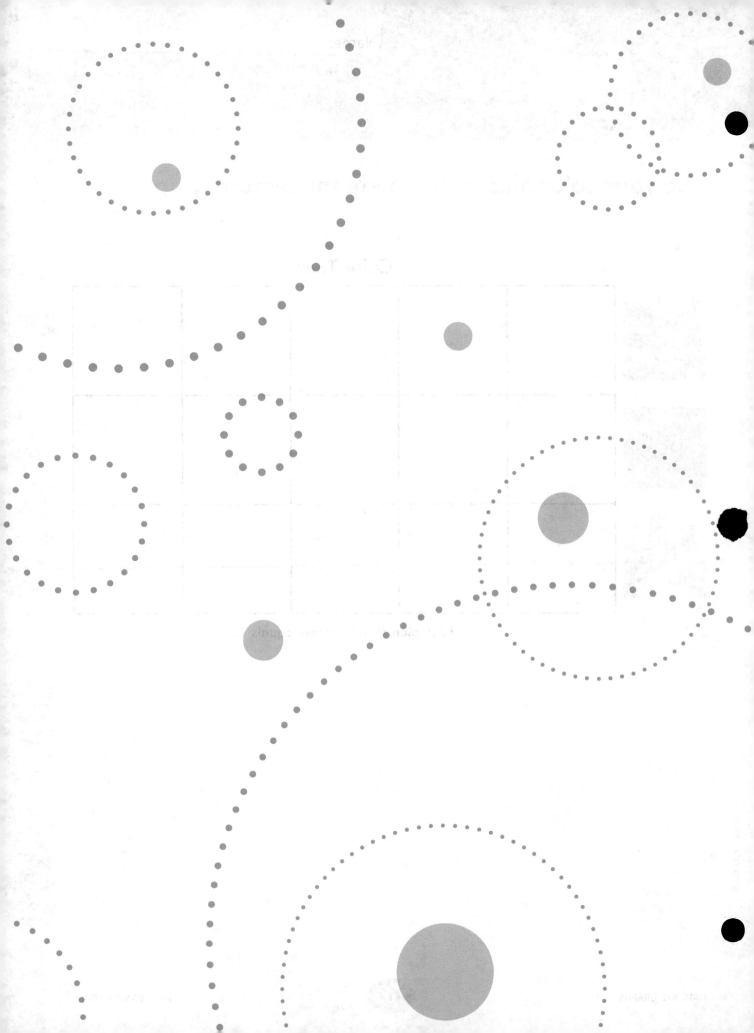

Ways to Show Data

The data show the favorite sport for 5 people.
Draw each sports ball in the left-hand column; in the
right-hand column, show how many people like
each sport.

Person Asked					
Favorite Sport					

Drawing of Ball	Number of People

TRY IT

Count how many bears there are of each color. Record the results in the picture graph. Write the title above the picture graph.

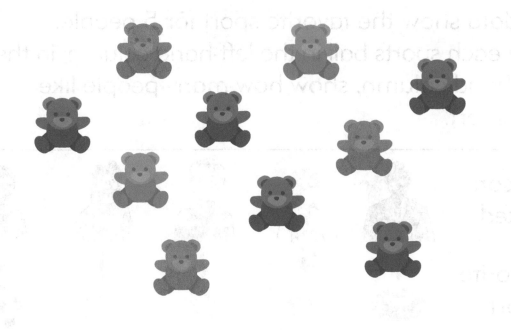

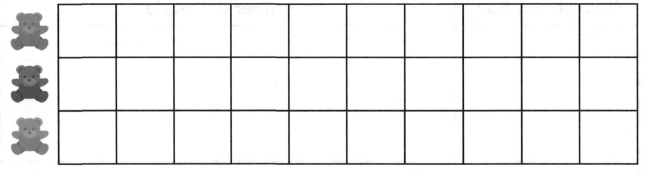

Each picture in the boxes equals 1.

TRY IT

Compare Data in a Picture Graph

Compare Data

Use the Favorite Flower graph for Problems 1–3.

Favorite Flower										

Each picture in the boxes equals 1.

1. Circle the flower that was picked the greatest number of times.

A.   B.   C.   D.

2. Circle the flower that was picked the least number of times.

A.   B.   C.   D.

3. Circle the two flowers that were picked the same number of times.

A.    B.    C.   D.

TRY IT

Use the Favorite Sport graph for Problems 4–6.

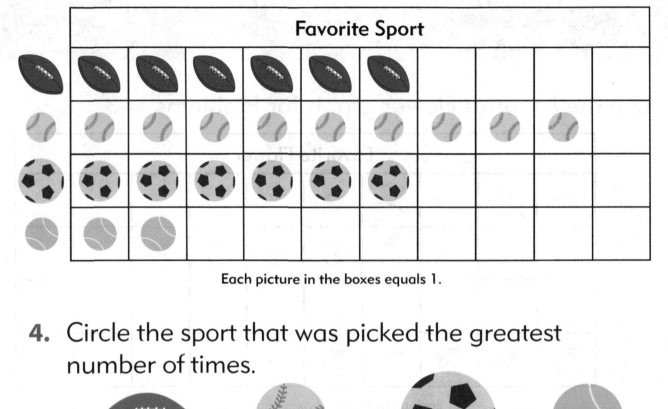

Favorite Sport

Each picture in the boxes equals 1.

4. Circle the sport that was picked the greatest number of times.

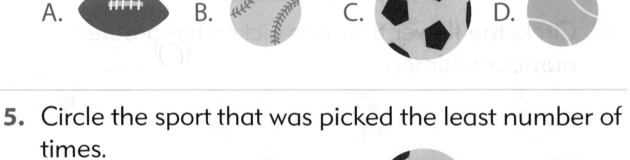

A.　　　　B.　　　　C.　　　　D.

5. Circle the sport that was picked the least number of times.

A.　　　　B.　　　　C.　　　　D.

6. Circle the two sports that were picked the same number of times.

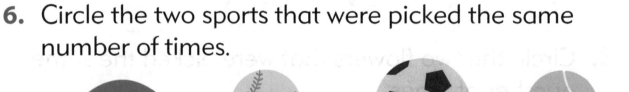

A.　　　　B.　　　　C.　　　　D.

TRY IT

Read each problem and circle the answer.

7. Look at the picture graph. Which animals are there the most of in the zoo?

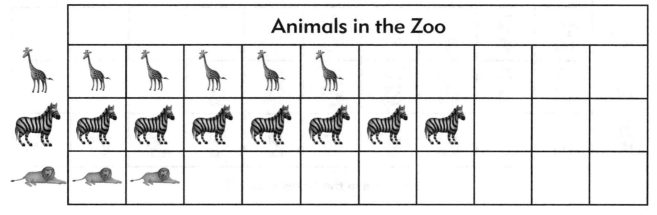

Animals in the Zoo

Each picture in the boxes equals 1.

A. giraffes   B. zebras   C. lions

---

8. Look at the picture graph. Which color flower do you see the most of in the graph?

Flowers

Each picture in the boxes equals 1.

A. red   B. pink   C. yellow

TRY IT

9. Look at the picture graph. Which drink was picked the most?

Favorite Drink

🥫	🥫	🥫	🥫	🥫	🥫					
🥫	🥫	🥫	🥫	🥫	🥫	🥫	🥫			
🥫	🥫	🥫	🥫	🥫	🥫	🥫	🥫	🥫	🥫	

Each picture in the boxes equals 1.

A. orange drink

B. green drink

C. purple drink

10. Look at the picture graph. Which drinks were picked an equal number of times?

Favorite Drink

🥫	🥫	🥫	🥫	🥫	🥫	🥫	🥫	🥫	🥫	🥫
🥫	🥫	🥫	🥫	🥫	🥫					
🥫	🥫	🥫	🥫	🥫	🥫	🥫	🥫	🥫	🥫	🥫

Each picture in the boxes equals 1.

A. red and orange drinks

B. red and yellow drinks

C. orange and yellow drinks

TRY IT

Interpret Picture Graphs
Compare Data in a Picture Graph

Use the data below to complete the Favorite Seasons picture graph.

Data			
Winter	Spring	Summer	Fall
❄	☂	🌻	🍃
4	4	7	3

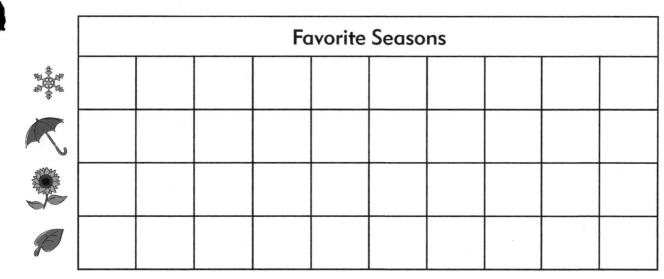

Each picture in the boxes equals 1.

L E A R N

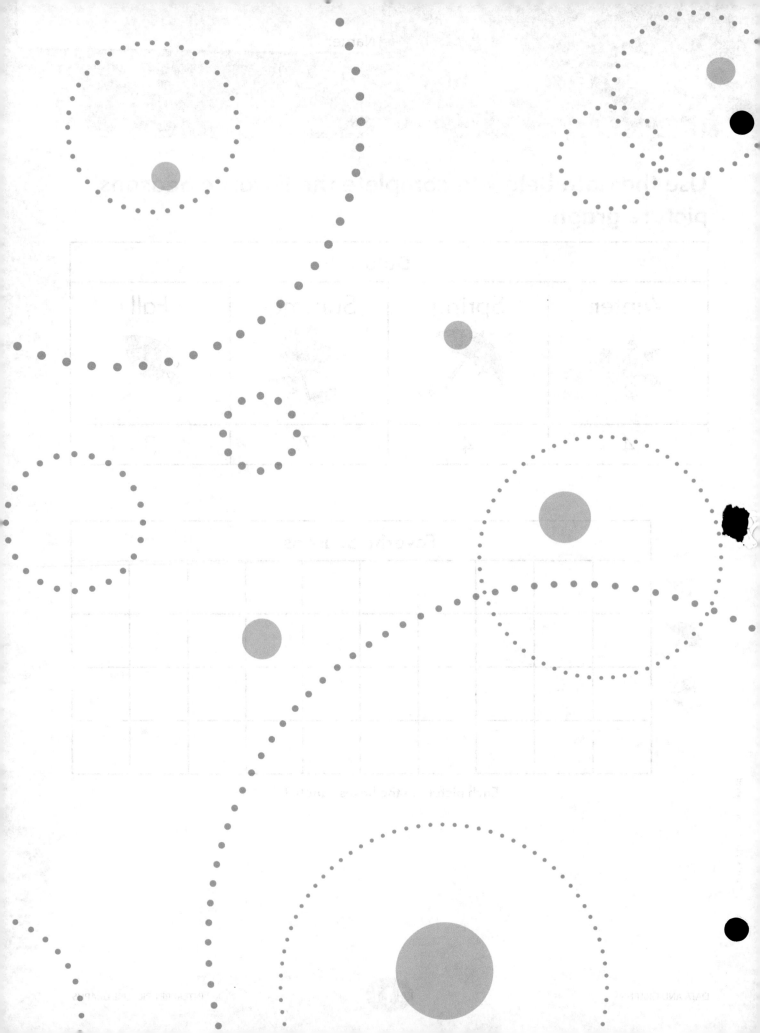

Interpret Picture Graphs

Picture Graph Data

Use the Favorite Toys picture graph for Problems 1–3.

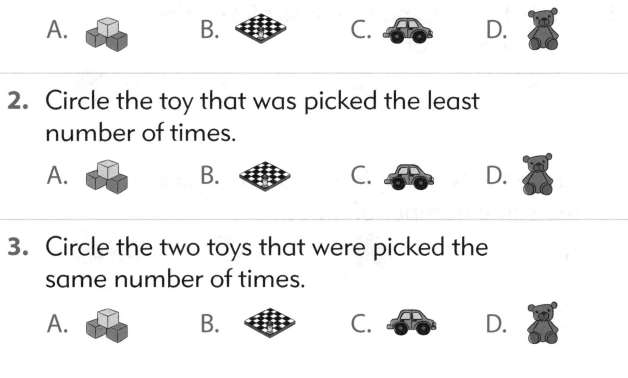

Favorite Toys

Each picture in the boxes equals 1.

1. Circle the toy that was picked the greatest number of times.

   A.   B.   C.   D.

2. Circle the toy that was picked the least number of times.

   A.   B.   C.   D.

3. Circle the two toys that were picked the same number of times.

   A.   B.   C.   D.

TRY IT

Use the Favorite Pizza Toppings picture graph for Problems 4–6.

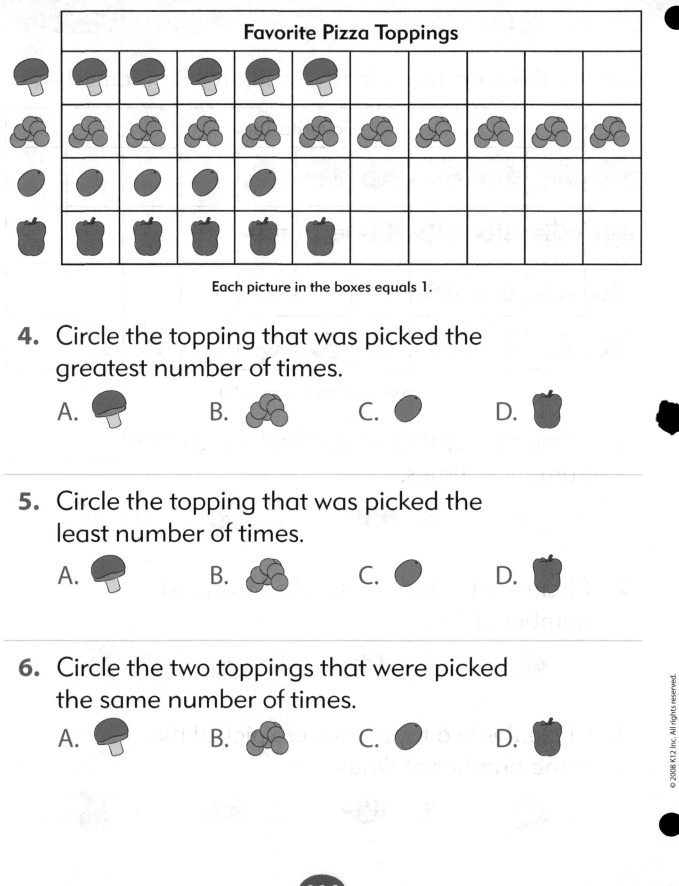

Each picture in the boxes equals 1.

4. Circle the topping that was picked the greatest number of times.

   A. [mushroom]   B. [olives]   C. [pepperoni]   D. [pepper]

5. Circle the topping that was picked the least number of times.

   A. [mushroom]   B. [olives]   C. [pepperoni]   D. [pepper]

6. Circle the two toppings that were picked the same number of times.

   A. [mushroom]   B. [olives]   C. [pepperoni]   D. [pepper]

TRY IT

Circle the answer.

7. Look at the Favorite Fruit picture graph. Which two fruits were picked the same number of times?

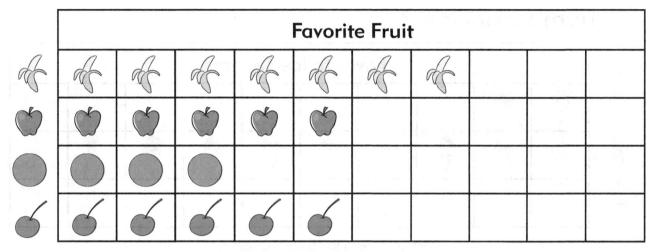

Each picture in the boxes equals 1.

A. banana and orange

B. apple and cherry

C. cherry and orange

---

8. Look at the Number of Pet Treats Eaten picture graph. Which pet ate the most treats?

Number of Pet Treats Eaten

Each picture in the boxes equals 1.

A. hamster B. cat C. bird D. frog

T R Y I T

Circle the answer.

9. Look at the Favorite Ice Cream picture graph below. Which ice cream flavor was picked the least number of times?

Each picture in the boxes equals 1.

A. mint ice cream

B. chocolate ice cream

C. strawberry ice cream

10. Look at the Favorite Ice Cream picture graph below. Which ice cream flavor was picked the greatest number of times?

Favorite Ice Cream

Each picture in the boxes equals 1.

A. vanilla ice cream

B. chocolate ice cream

C. blueberry ice cream

Name:

Answer Data Questions

Favorite Snacks

Use the picture graph to answer Problems 1–4.
Write the answer on the line.

Students' Favorite Snacks										
🥨	🥨	🥨	🥨							
▪	▪	▪	▪	▪	▪	▪				
⬤	⬤									

Each picture in the boxes equals 1.

1. How many students like raisins best?

    _____

2. How many students like pretzels best?

    _____

3. How many more students chose raisins than crackers?

    _____

4. How many students answered the question "What is your favorite snack?"

    _____

5. Look at the picture graph. How many snails are in the aquarium? Circle the answer.

Sea Animals in the Aquarium										
★	★	★								
🐟	🐟	🐟	🐟	🐟	🐟	🐟				
🐌	🐌	🐌	🐌	🐌	🐌	🐌	🐌			

Each picture in the boxes equals 1.

A. 2   B. 6   C. 7

TRY IT

Use the picture graph to answer Problems 6 and 7.

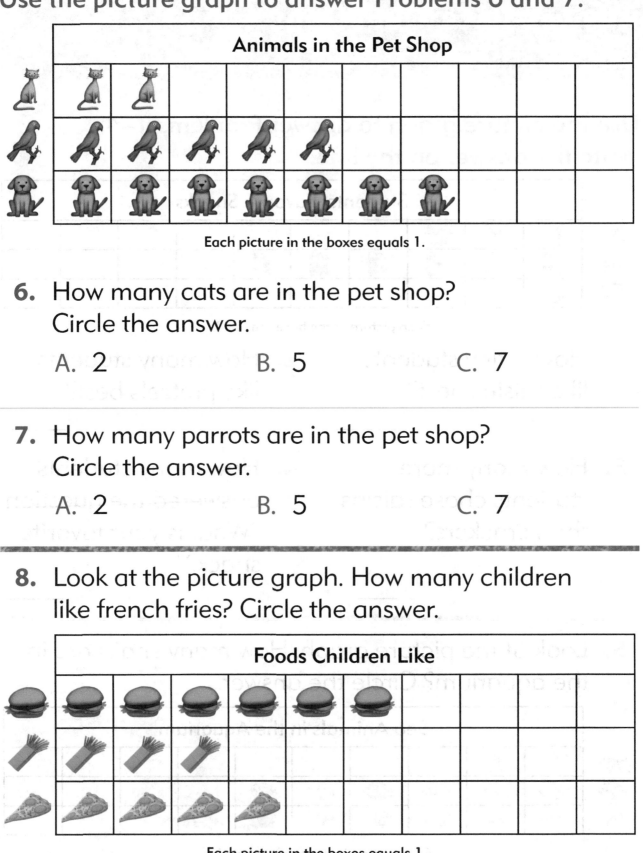

Animals in the Pet Shop

Each picture in the boxes equals 1.

6. How many cats are in the pet shop?
   Circle the answer.

   A. 2   B. 5   C. 7

7. How many parrots are in the pet shop?
   Circle the answer.

   A. 2   B. 5   C. 7

8. Look at the picture graph. How many children
   like french fries? Circle the answer.

Foods Children Like

Each picture in the boxes equals 1.

   A. 3   B. 4   C. 6

TRY IT

Name: _____

Unit Review

Checkpoint Practice

Use this group of pictures for Problems 1–3.

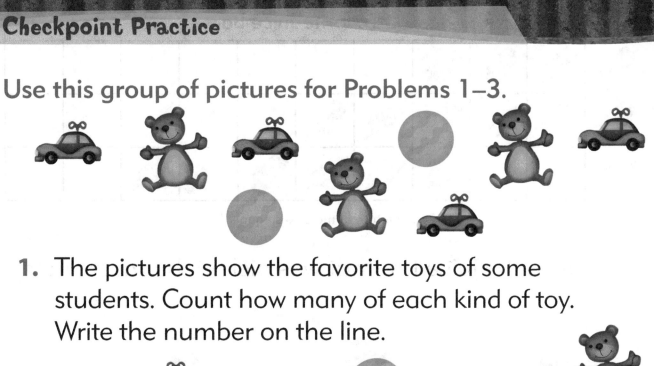

1. The pictures show the favorite toys of some students. Count how many of each kind of toy. Write the number on the line.

_____   _____ ⬤   _____ 🧸

2. How would you figure out how many of each color toy you have?

3. Use your data from Problem 1 to make a picture graph. Draw pictures to show how many of each toy.

Favorite Toys								

Each picture in the boxes equals 1.

UNIT REVIEW

Use the picture graph below for Problems 4–6.

Favorite Juice Bar

Each picture in the boxes equals 1.

4. Circle the juice bar that was picked the most times.

5. Circle the juice bar that was picked the fewest times.

6. How many more students picked  than  ?

_____

UNIT REVIEW

Read each problem and follow the directions.

7. How would you figure out which eye color is most common in your family?

8. How would you figure out how many different colors of shoes you have?

9. Look at the group of shapes below. Count how many of each shape. Write the number on the line.

____ △   ____ ▪   ____ ⬤

Read each problem and follow the directions.

10. Which group has the same data as the data shown? Circle the answer.

A.

B.

C.

11. Ask 5 friends or family members what their favorite dessert is. Draw a picture of each dessert that they name. Next to each picture, write the number that tells how many people picked that dessert.

12. Which picture graph best shows the data for favorite foods? Circle the answer.

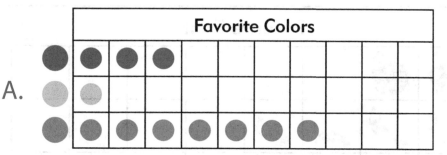

Favorite Colors

A.

Each picture in the boxes equals 1.

Favorite Sports

B.

Each picture in the boxes equals 1.

Favorite Food

C.

Each picture in the boxes equals 1.

13. Which color was picked most? Circle the row.

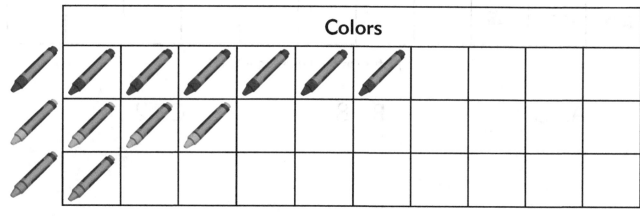

Colors

Each picture in the boxes equals 1.

UNIT REVIEW

14. Look at the picture graph. How many more people liked bananas best than liked oranges best? Circle the answer.

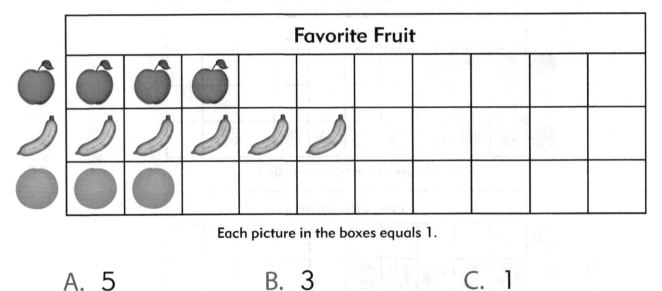

Favorite Fruit

Each picture in the boxes equals 1.

A. 5   B. 3   C. 1

15. Look at the picture graph. How many giraffes are there in the zoo? Circle the answer.

Animals in the Zoo

Each picture in the boxes equals 1.

A. 5   B. 8   C. 2

Count Aloud Through 20

Numbers Through 20

Read each problem and follow the directions.

1. Count. How many giraffes are there?
Circle the answer.

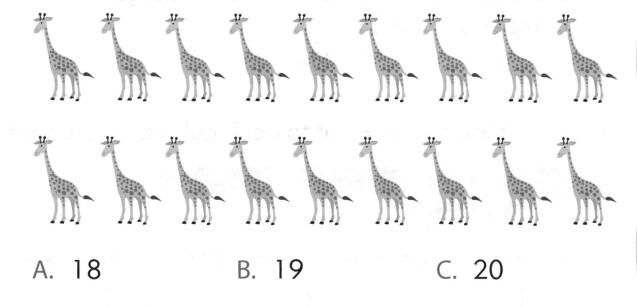

A. 18   B. 19   C. 20

2. Count. How many zebras are there?
Circle the answer.

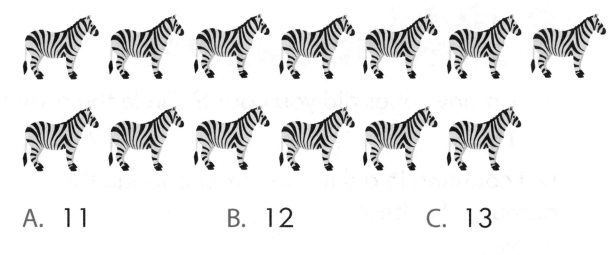

A. 11   B. 12   C. 13

TRY IT

3. Count the cubes. Point to each cube as you count it.

How many cubes did you count? Circle the answer.

A. 12　　　　　　　B. 13　　　　　　　C. 14

Count the cubes in a different order.
Did counting in a different order change the number of cubes?

A. Yes　　　　　　B. No

---

4. Count the cubes. Point to each cube as you count it.

How many cubes did you count? Circle the answer.

A. 15　　　　　　　B. 16　　　　　　　C. 17

The cubes are in a different order.
Count the cubes again.

How many cubes did you count? Circle the answer.

A. 15　　　　　　　B. 16　　　　　　　C. 17

Did counting in a different order change the number of cubes?

A. Yes　　　　　　B. No

TRY IT

5. Count aloud. How many polar bears are there? Say the number.

6. Count aloud. How many pandas are there? Say the number

7. The pandas eat bamboo. Count aloud the bamboo sticks. Circle the number that tells how many.

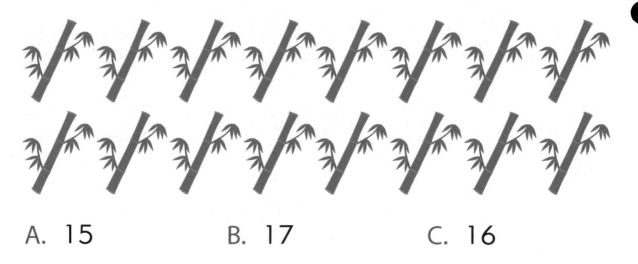

A. 15   B. 17   C. 16

---

8. Count the alligators. Start at the red arrow and count to the right. Then count them again. Start at the blue arrow and count to the left. What happened to the number of alligators when you counted from the right and then counted from the left? Circle the answer.

A. The number stayed the same.

B. The number went up one.

C. The number changed.

TRY IT

Represent an Amount Through 20

Amounts Through 20

Read each problem and follow the directions.

1. Draw 13 circles.

2. Draw 19 squares.

3. Show 14 cubes.

4. Show 16 cubes.

TRY IT

5. Show 10 cubes.

6. Show 12 cubes.

7. Madison has 11 bananas. Draw shapes on the fruit plate to show all of her bananas.

8. Troy has 18 golf balls. Draw shapes on the putting green to show the golf balls.

TRY IT

Read each problem and follow the directions.

1. Count aloud the butterflies. First count the butterflies in the tree. Then count the butterflies in the air.

   How many butterflies are there?

   Circle the answer.

   A. 13

   B. 14

   C. 15

2. Count aloud the raindrops. Cross out each raindrop as you count it.

   How many raindrops are falling from the cloud?

   Write the number.

   _____

   _ _ _ _ _

   _____

T R Y   I T

3. Count aloud. How many flowers are there?
Circle the answer.

A. 10

B. 11

C. 12

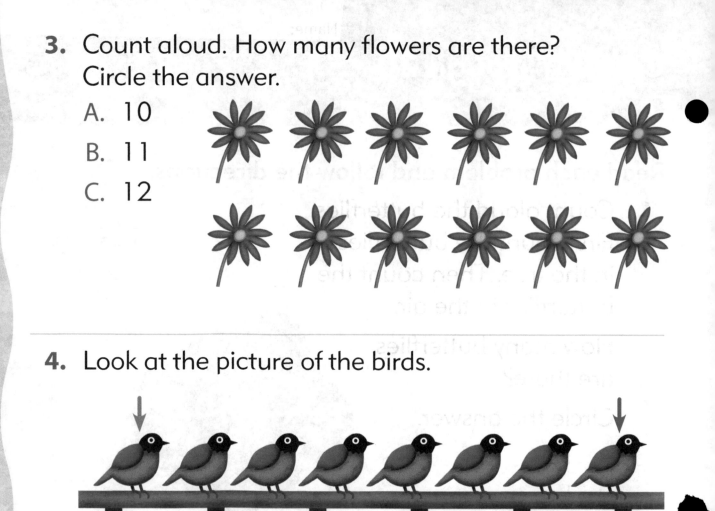

4. Look at the picture of the birds.

Start with the blue arrow.
Count the birds.

_____

How many birds did you count?
Write the number.

- - - -

_____

Start with the red arrow. Count again.

_____

How many birds did you count?
Write the number.

- - - -

_____

Show Amounts Through 20

Represent with Drawings

Make a drawing to show each amount.

1. Draw 11 lines.

---

2. Draw 14 lines.

---

3. Draw 17 lines.

---

4. Draw 20 lines.

---

5. Draw 12 lines.

LEARN

6. Draw 16 dots.

7. Draw 19 dots.

8. Draw 13 dots.

9. Draw 15 dots.

10. There are 18 dots.

● ● ● ● ● ● ● ● ●
● ● ● ● ● ● ● ● ●

Make a drawing to show 18 in a different way.

Compare Sets Through 20

Compare Two or More Sets

1. Circle the group that has more straw hats.
   Then draw an X on the group with fewer straw hats.

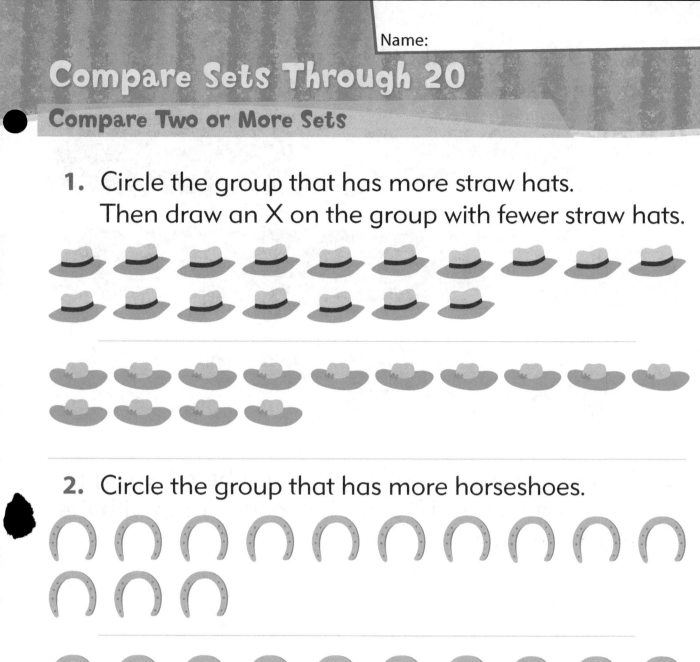

2. Circle the group that has more horseshoes.

3. Jimmy watered 15 corn plants.
   Sam watered 16 corn plants.

   Who watered more plants? Circle the answer.

   A. Sam   B. Jimmy

LEARN

4. Circle the groups that have the same number of hay bales.

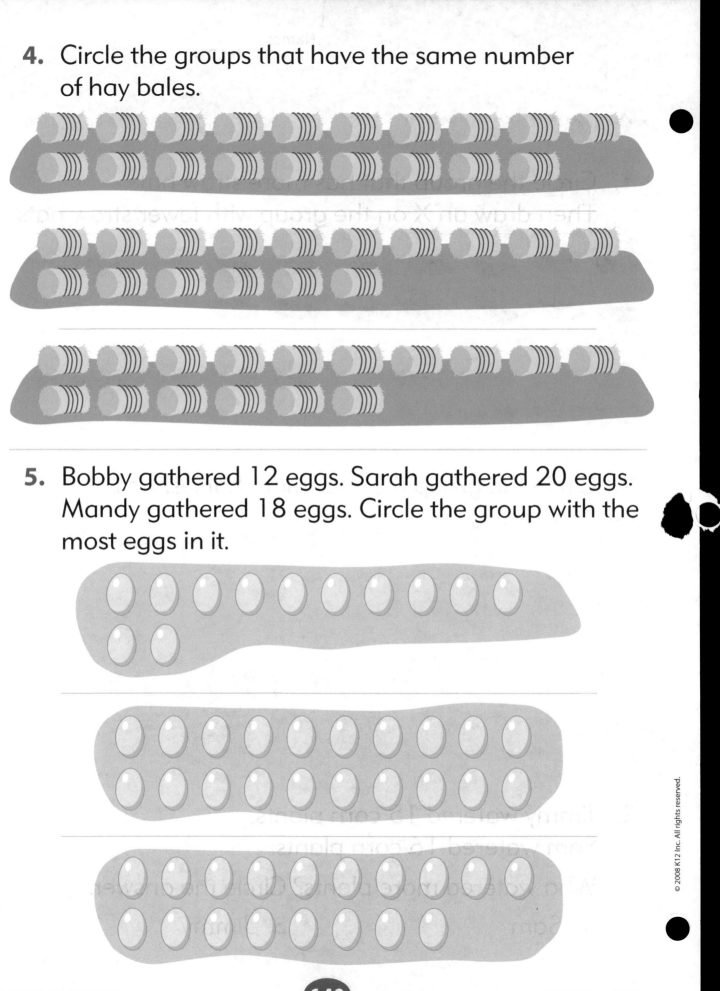

5. Bobby gathered 12 eggs. Sarah gathered 20 eggs. Mandy gathered 18 eggs. Circle the group with the most eggs in it.

Make Sets

Name: _____

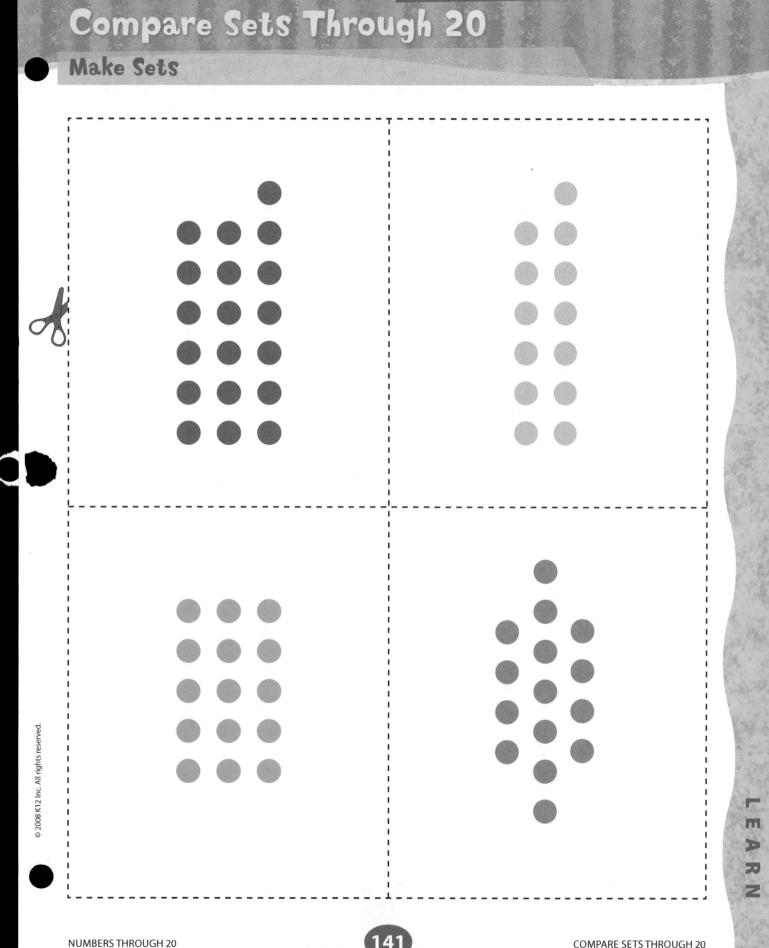

LEARN

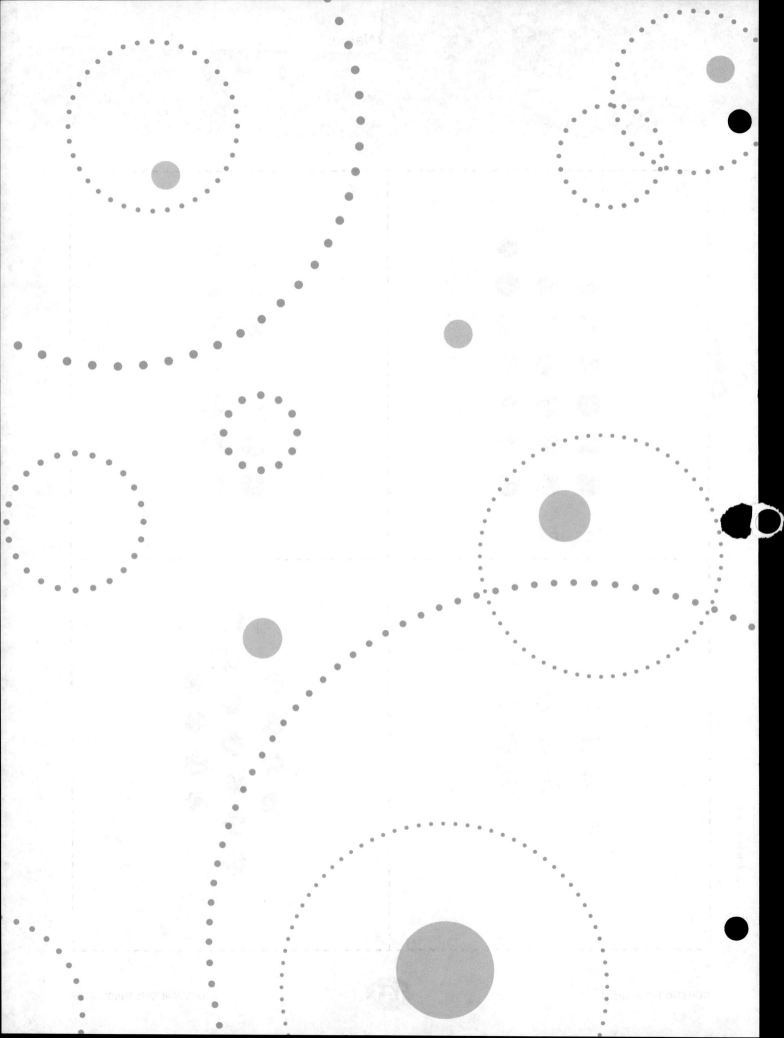

Compare Sets Through 20

Compare Sets

1. Circle the group that has more hats.

2. Circle the set with the most eggs. Then draw an X on the set with the fewest eggs.

3. Draw a circle around the group with the fewest flowers in it.

T R Y   I T

4. Shannon picked 17 apples. Jordan picked 20 apples. Which child picked fewer apples?

Circle the set with fewer apples.

5. Draw a circle around the set that has the most cows.

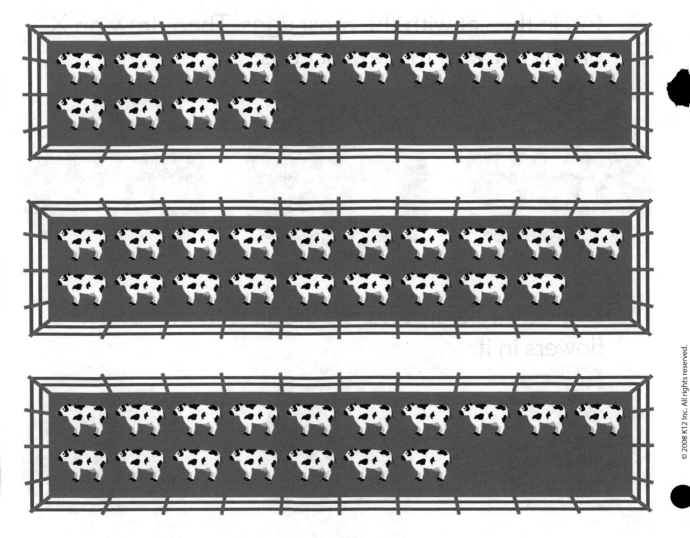

TRY IT

Write Numerals Through 20

See, Feel, and Write 1-20

Count the objects. Write the number to show how many objects are in each group.

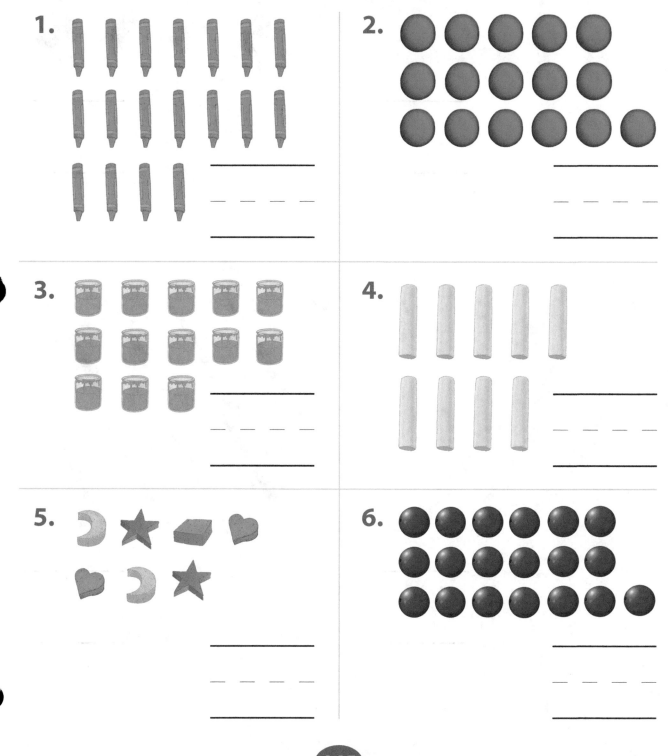

1.

2.

3.

4.

5.

6.

L E A R N

Count the objects. Write the number to show how many objects are in each group.

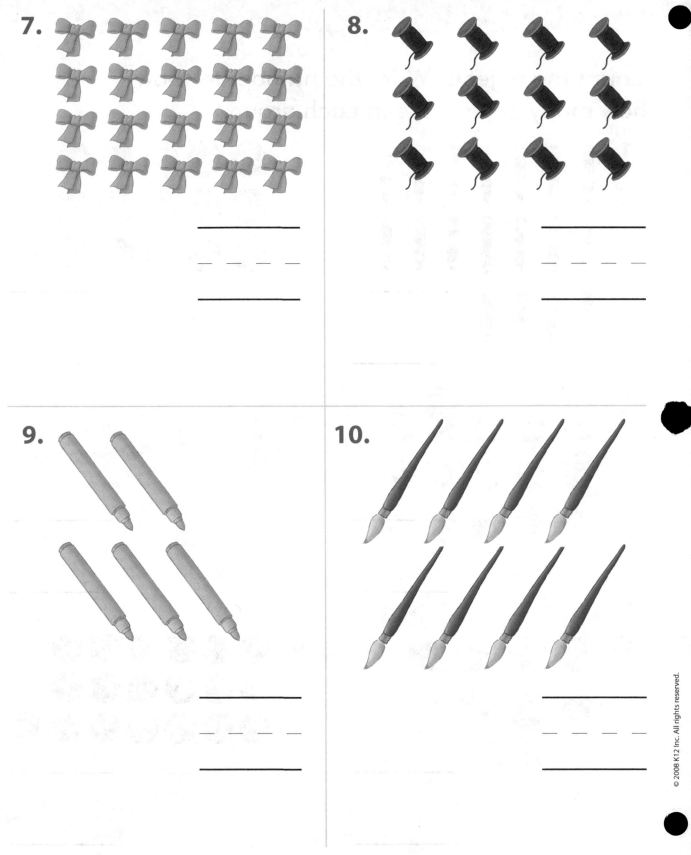

7.

_____
- - - - - -
_____

8.

_____
- - - - - -
_____

9.

_____
- - - - - -
_____

10.

_____
- - - - - -
_____

Write Numerals Through 20

Count and Write 1-20

Write the number to show how many objects are in each group.

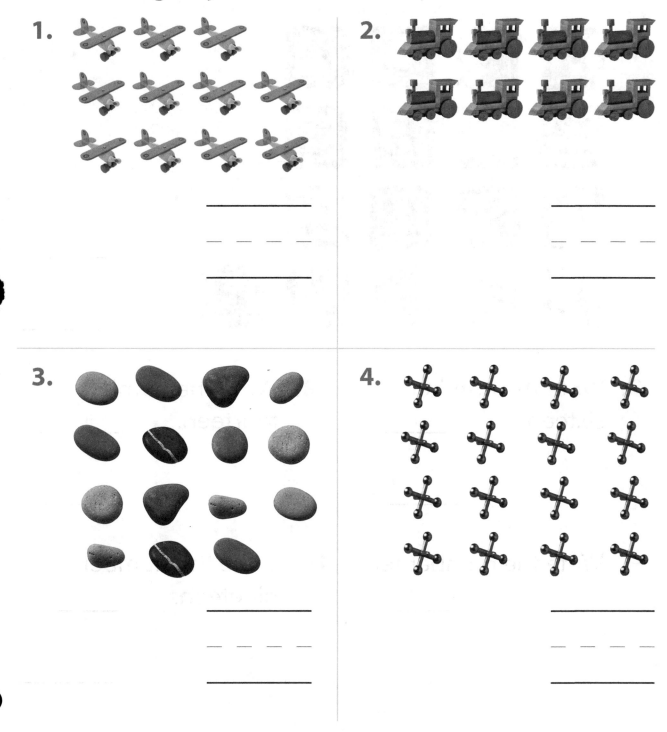

1.

2.

3.

4.

T R Y   I T

147

5.

_____

- - - - - -

_____

6.

_____

- - - - - -

_____

7. Write the number
sixteen.

_____

- - - - - -

_____

8. Write the number
fourteen.

_____

- - - - - -

_____

9. Write the number ten.

_____

- - - - - -

_____

10. Write the number
nineteen.

_____

- - - - - -

_____

T R Y   I T

Compare Numbers and Sets Through 20

Greater and Lesser Values

1. Circle the hive with fewer bees.

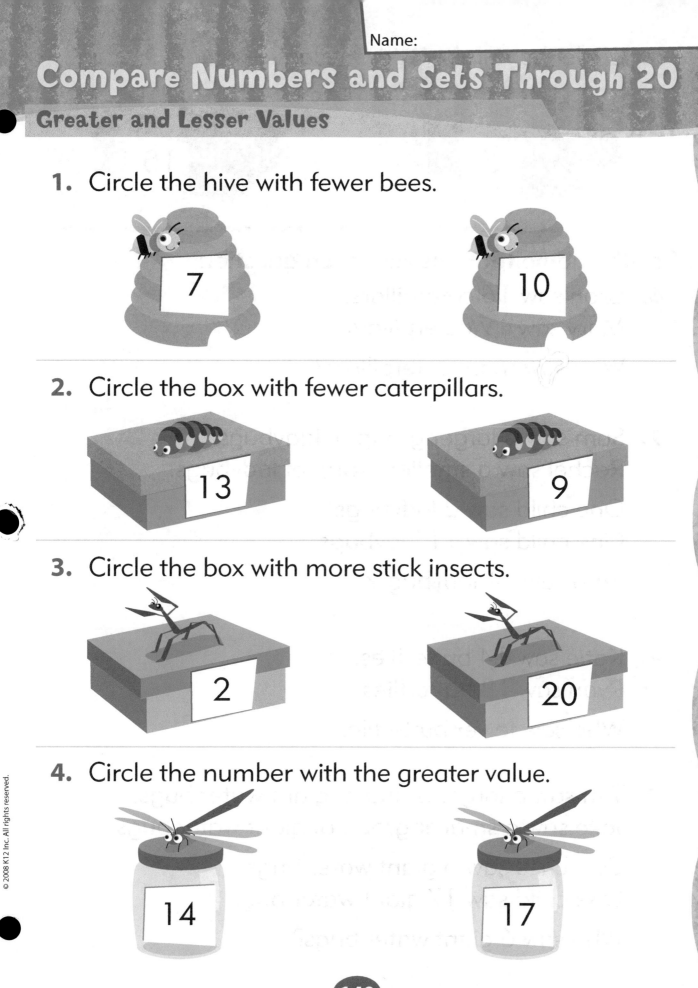

2. Circle the box with fewer caterpillars.

3. Circle the box with more stick insects.

4. Circle the number with the greater value.

L E A R N

5. Circle the number with the lesser value.

5

15

Say the name that answers each question.

6. Leon saw 16 caterpillars.
Mary saw 19 caterpillars.

Who saw more caterpillars?

7. Sam saw a larger group of ladybugs.
Rachel saw a smaller group of ladybugs.

One child saw 2 ladybugs.
One child saw 11 ladybugs.

Who saw 11 ladybugs?

8. Katie saw 14 butterflies.
Ryan saw 18 butterflies.

Who saw fewer butterflies?

9. Tim saw a larger group of giant water bugs.
Jake saw a smaller group of giant water bugs.

One child saw 6 giant water bugs.
One child saw 17 giant water bugs.

Who saw 6 giant water bugs?

Name:

Compare Numbers and Sets Through 20

Compare Numbers Through 20

1. Circle the jar with more butterflies.

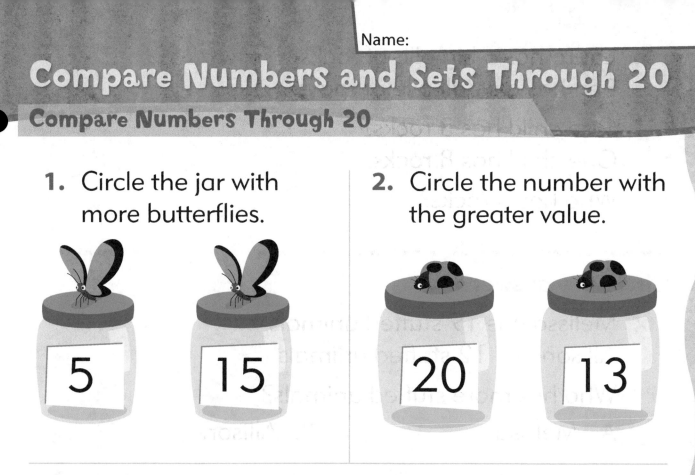

2. Circle the number with the greater value.

5   15   20   13

3. Circle the number with the lesser value.

10

16

Say the name that answers each question.

4. Cody saw 12 caterpillars.
Max saw 5 caterpillars.

Who saw more caterpillars?

T R Y I T

5. Laura has a big pile of rocks.
Ben has a small pile of rocks.

One child has 3 rocks.
One child has 8 rocks.

Who has 3 rocks?

Circle the answer.

6. Melissa has 19 stuffed animals.
Allison has 12 stuffed animals.

Who has more stuffed animals?

A. Melissa   B. Allison

---

7. Jaime has 12 goldfish.
Michael has 17 goldfish.

Who has more goldfish?

A. Jaime   B. Michael

---

8. Which group has more balls?

A. ●●●●●●●●
8

B. ●●●●●●●●●●●●●●
14

TRY IT

Write Numerals from 1 Through 20

Trace and Write Through 20

Trace each number with a glue stick. Then cover the number and the glue with a piece of yarn.

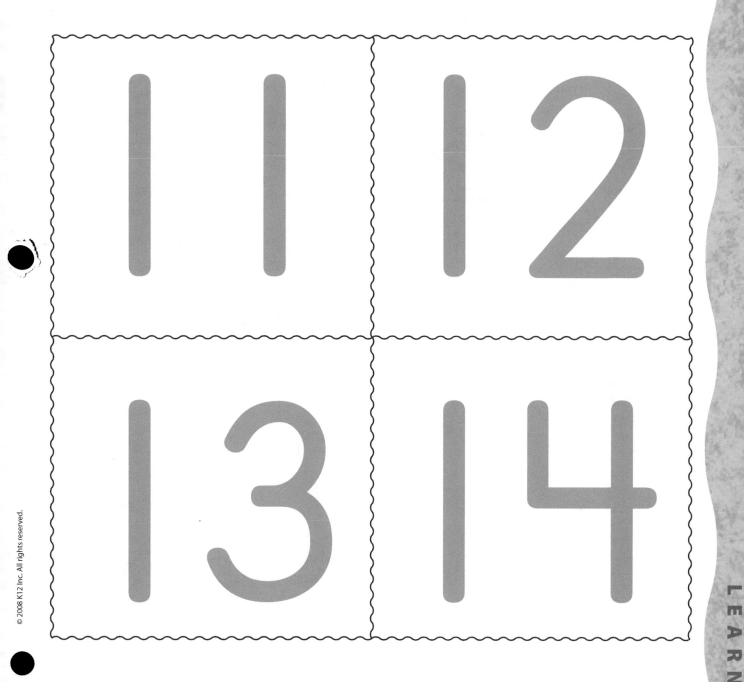

L E A R N

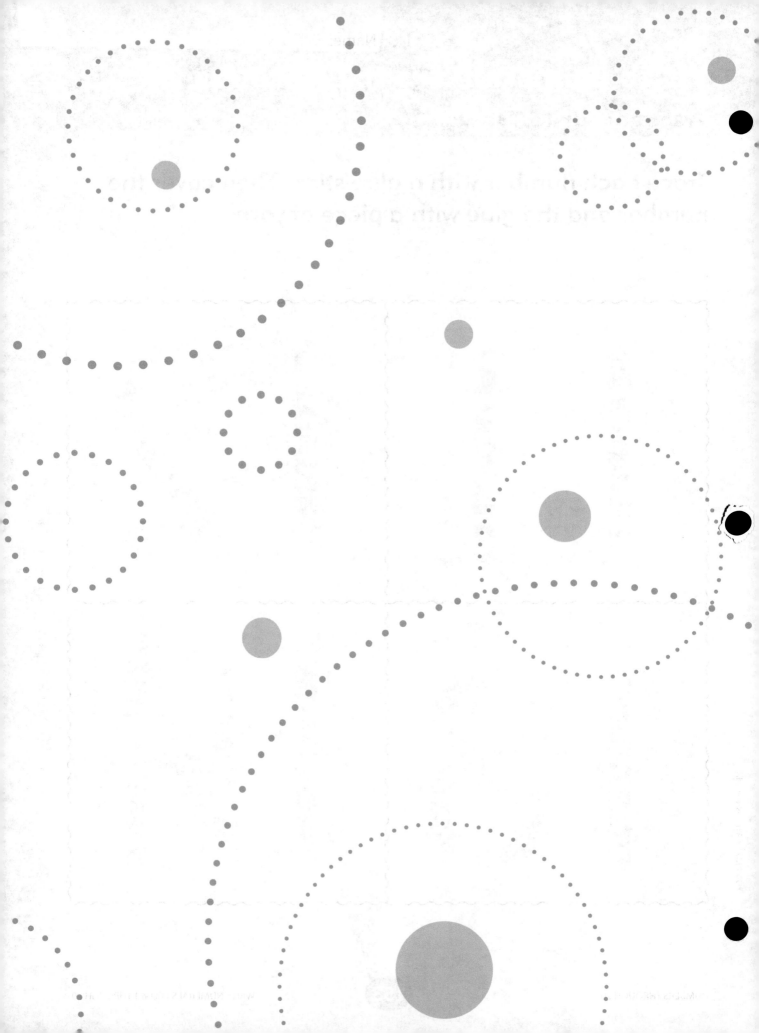

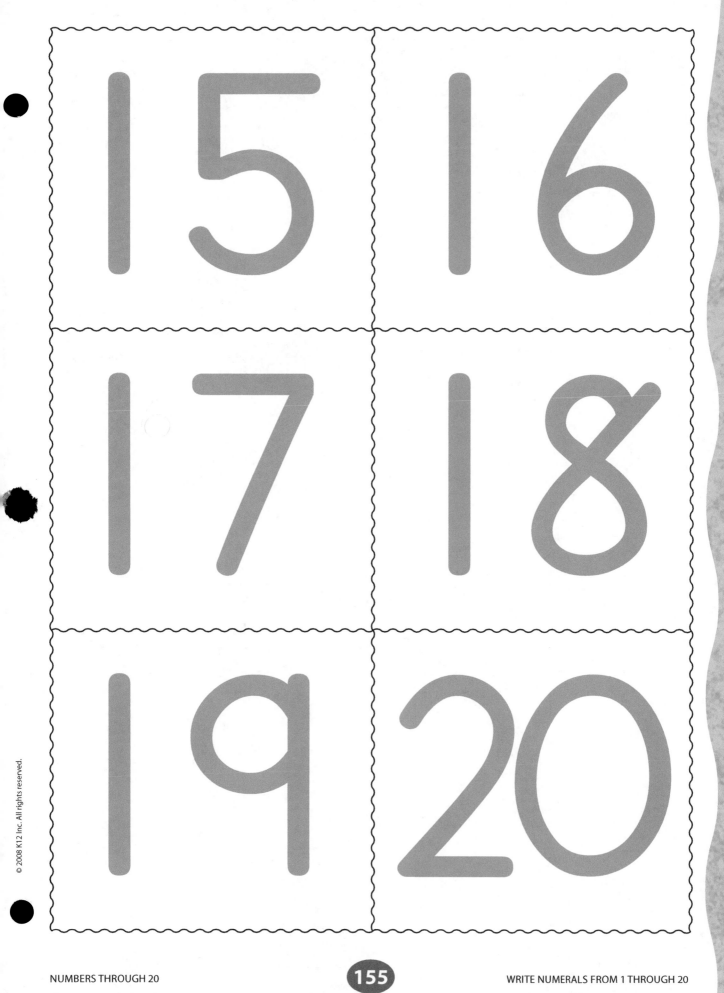

LEARN

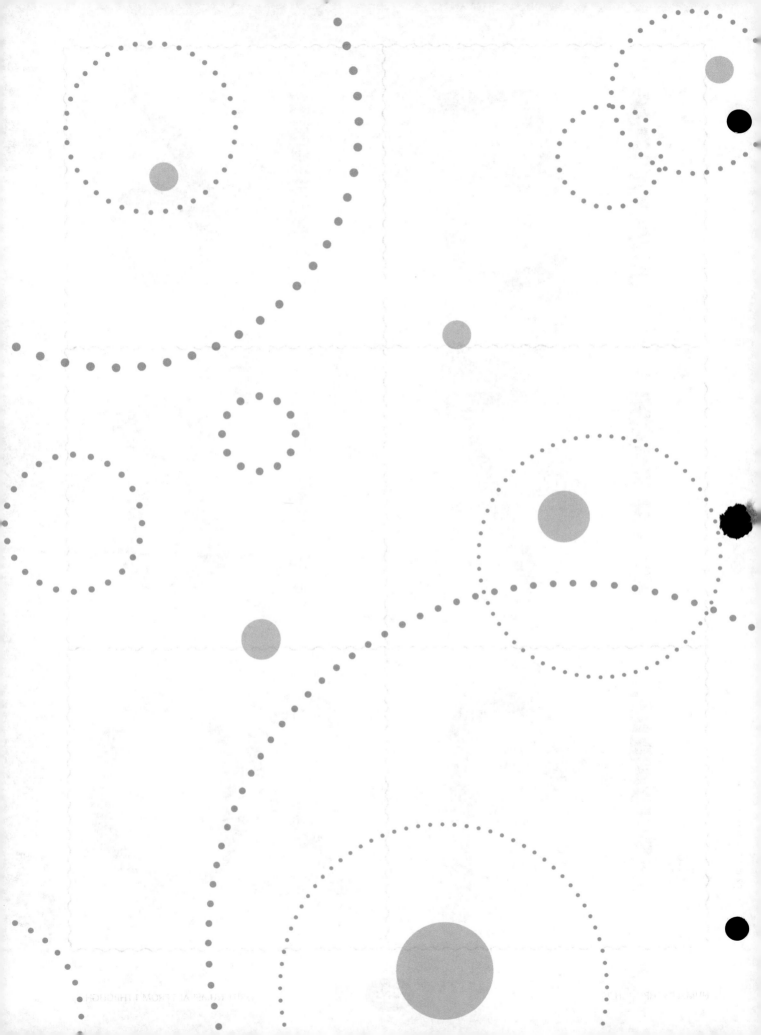

Write Numerals from 1 Through 20

Write Numbers Through 20

Write the number of objects shown in each picture.

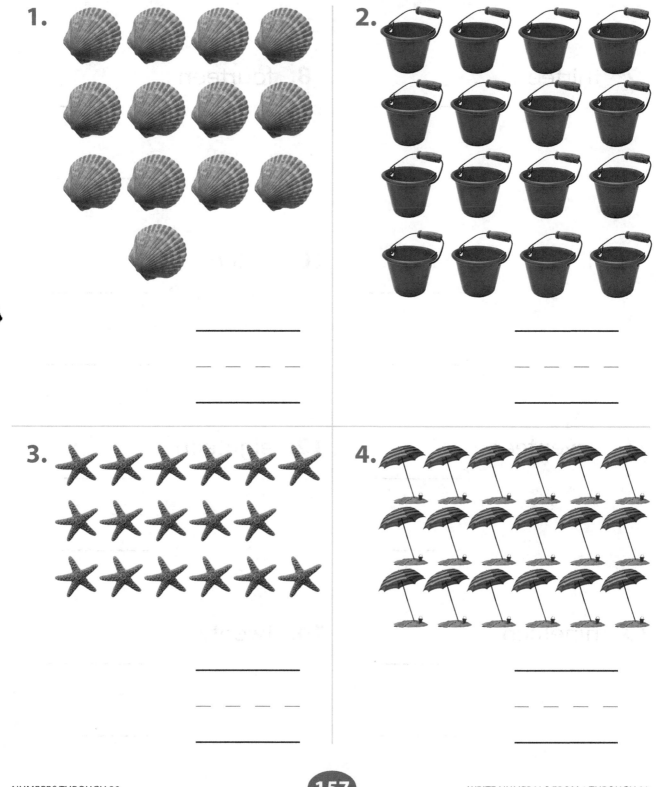

1.

2.

3.

4.

_____

- - - - - - - -

_____

T R Y   I T

Write the number for each word.

5. eleven

_____

- - - - - - -

_____

6. twelve

_____

- - - - - - -

_____

7. thirteen

_____

- - - - - - -

_____

8. fourteen

_____

- - - - - - -

_____

9. fifteen

_____

- - - - - - -

_____

10. sixteen

_____

- - - - - - -

_____

11. seventeen

_____

- - - - - - -

_____

12. eighteen

_____

- - - - - - -

_____

13. nineteen

_____

- - - - - - -

_____

14. twenty

_____

- - - - - - -

_____

Name:

Read each problem and follow the directions.

1. Look at the bugs below. Count the bugs in the circle, and then count on the bugs in the square.

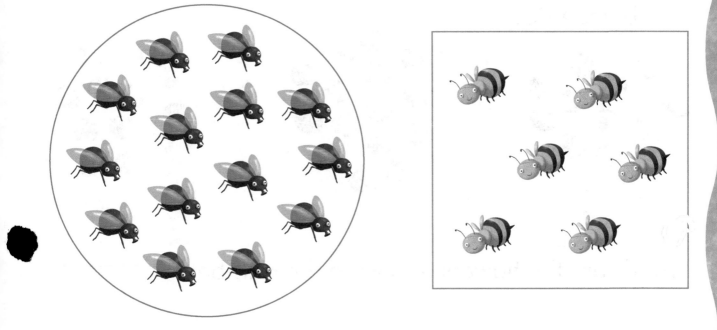

Now count the bugs in the square, and then count on the bugs in the circle.

Did the number of bugs change? Circle the answer.

A. Yes   B. No

2. Draw 18 dots.

3. Circle the group with more fruit.

4. Circle the two groups with the same number of blueberries.

5. Count the flowers and write the number.   ‾‾‾‾‾‾

‾ ‾ ‾ ‾

‾‾‾‾‾‾

6. Say the name to answer the question.
Chad saw 13 kites. Cole saw 17 kites.

Who saw more kites?

Count On to Add

Add on a Number Line

Use your number line to answer the problem.
Circle the answer.

1. Add 5 and 6.
   A. 9   B. 10   C. 11

2. Add 8 and 1.
   A. 8   B. 9   C. 10

Read each problem. Draw jumps on the number line to show how to add. Write numbers over the jumps to show each number you add and the sum.

3. Add 5 and 7.

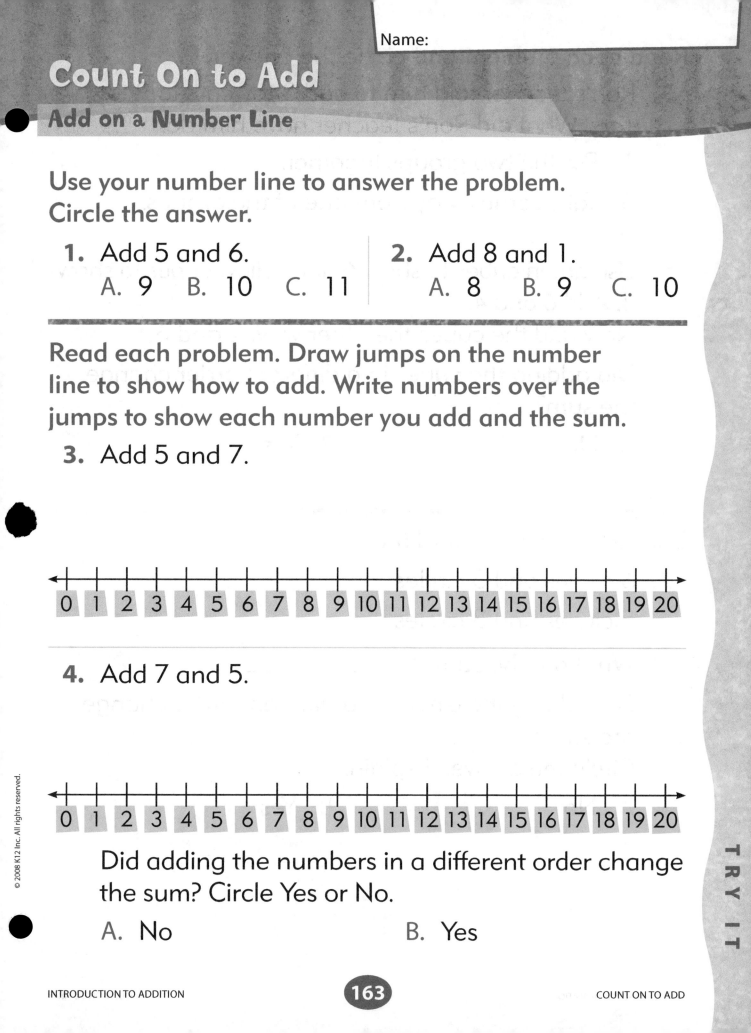

4. Add 7 and 5.

Did adding the numbers in a different order change the sum? Circle Yes or No.

   A. No

   B. Yes

TRY IT

Read each problem and circle the answer.

5. Ron's teacher told him to add 3 toy cars to 9 toy cars. What did Ron's teacher have him do?

   A. Put the two groups together.

   B. Take some away from one of the groups.

6. Use green cubes to show 6 and yellow cubes to show 4. Add 6 and 4.
   Now add the cubes the other way: 4 and 6.

   Did adding the cubes in a different order change the sum?

   A. No   B. Yes

Use circle blocks to find the sum.

7. 3 circles and 5 circles
   5 circles and 3 circles

   What are the sums? _____ ; _____

   Did adding the circles in a different order change the sum?
   Circle the answer. Explain.

   A. No   B. Yes

TRY IT

Count On

Count On by One and Two

Use the red and blue circles to count on by 1 or 2.
Then circle the answer.

1. Find the sum of 13 and 1.

    A. 13   B. 14   C. 15

2. Find the sum of 9 and 2.

    A. 10   B. 11   C. 12

3. Find the sum of 5 and 1.

    A. 4   B. 5   C. 6

4. Find the sum of 11 and 2.

    A. 11   B. 12   C. 13

5. Find the sum of 8 and 2.

    A. 8   B. 9   C. 10

6. Find the sum of 12 and 2.

    A. 13   B. 14   C. 15

TRY IT

Use the red and blue circles to count on by 1 or 2.
Then say the answer.

7. Find the sum of 6 and 2.

_____

8. Find the sum of 13 and 1.

_____

9. Find the sum of 13 and 2.

Circle the answer.

10. Which shows how to add 2 and 6?

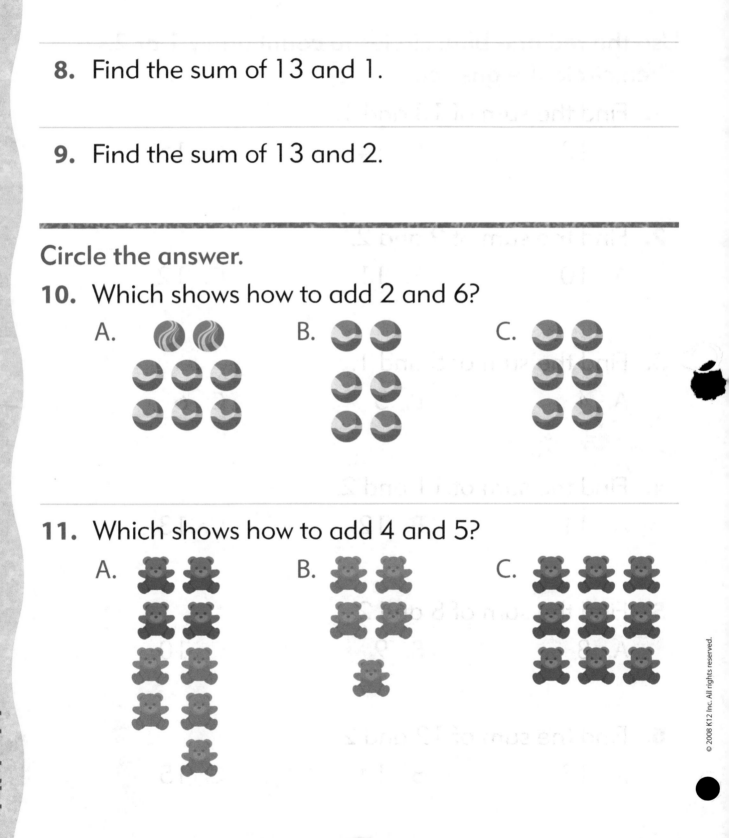

A.

B.

C.

11. Which shows how to add 4 and 5?

A.

B.

C.

TRY IT

Add with Models
More Ways to Model

Look at the domino tile. Use the number lines to show how to add the dots. Write the number above the arc. Then write the sum.

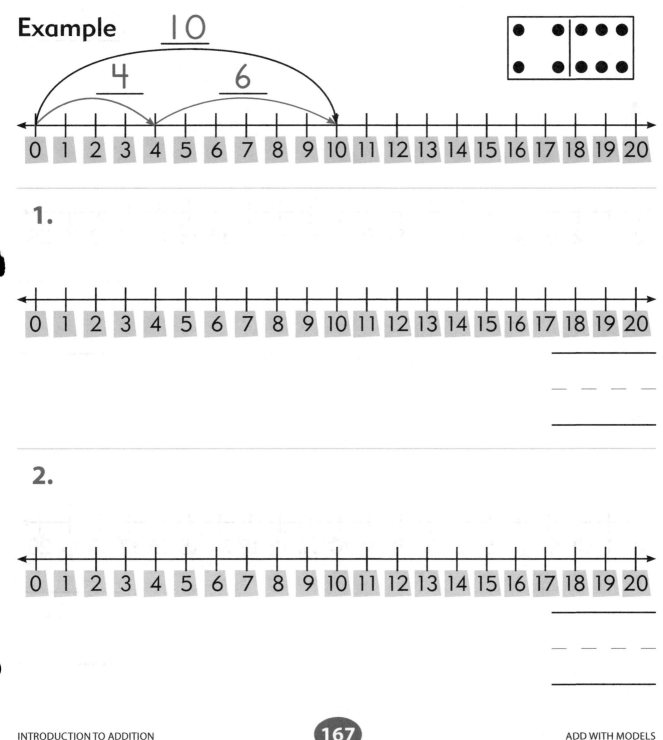

Example 10
4   6

0 1 2 3 4 5 6 7 8 9 10 11 12 13 14 15 16 17 18 19 20

1.

0 1 2 3 4 5 6 7 8 9 10 11 12 13 14 15 16 17 18 19 20

_____
_ _ _ _
_____

2.

0 1 2 3 4 5 6 7 8 9 10 11 12 13 14 15 16 17 18 19 20

_____
_ _ _ _
_____

L E A R N

3.

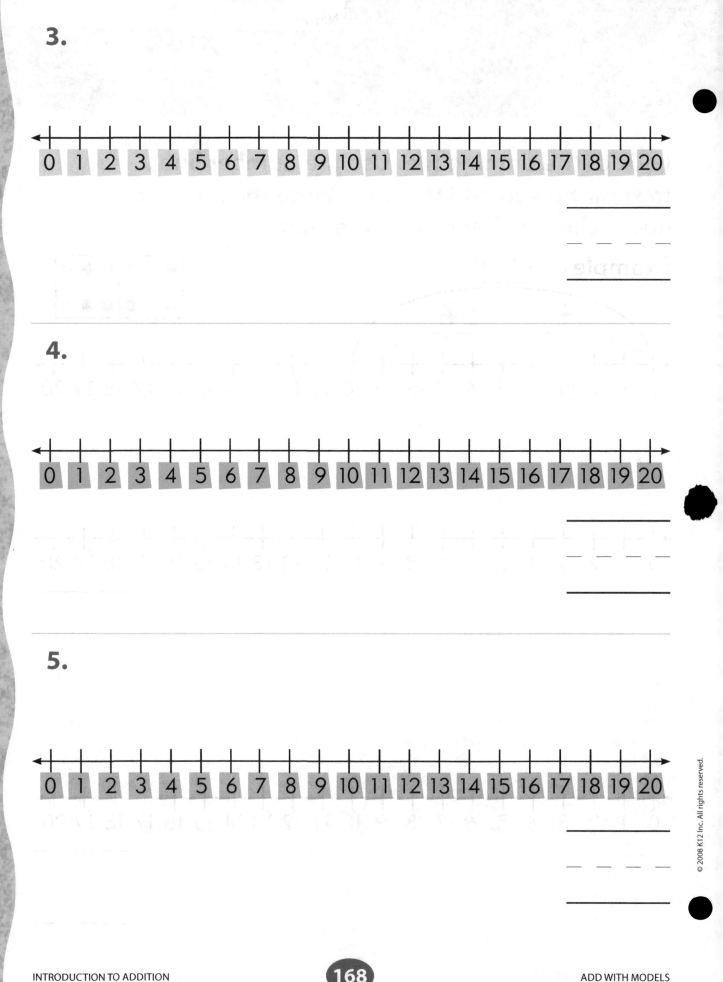

0 1 2 3 4 5 6 7 8 9 10 11 12 13 14 15 16 17 18 19 20

_____

- - - - -

_____

4.

0 1 2 3 4 5 6 7 8 9 10 11 12 13 14 15 16 17 18 19 20

_____

- - - - -

_____

5.

0 1 2 3 4 5 6 7 8 9 10 11 12 13 14 15 16 17 18 19 20

_____

- - - - -

_____

Add with Models

Find the Sum

Read each problem. Use arcs to show the numbers you add. Then show an arc for the sum. Write the sum above the arc.

1. Show how to add 6 and 10 on the number line.

```
0 1 2 3 4 5 6 7 8 9 10 11 12 13 14 15 16 17 18 19 20
```

2. Show how to add 8 and 6 on the number line.

```
0 1 2 3 4 5 6 7 8 9 10 11 12 13 14 15 16 17 18 19 20
```

T R Y   I T

3. Show how to add 9 and 3 on the number line.

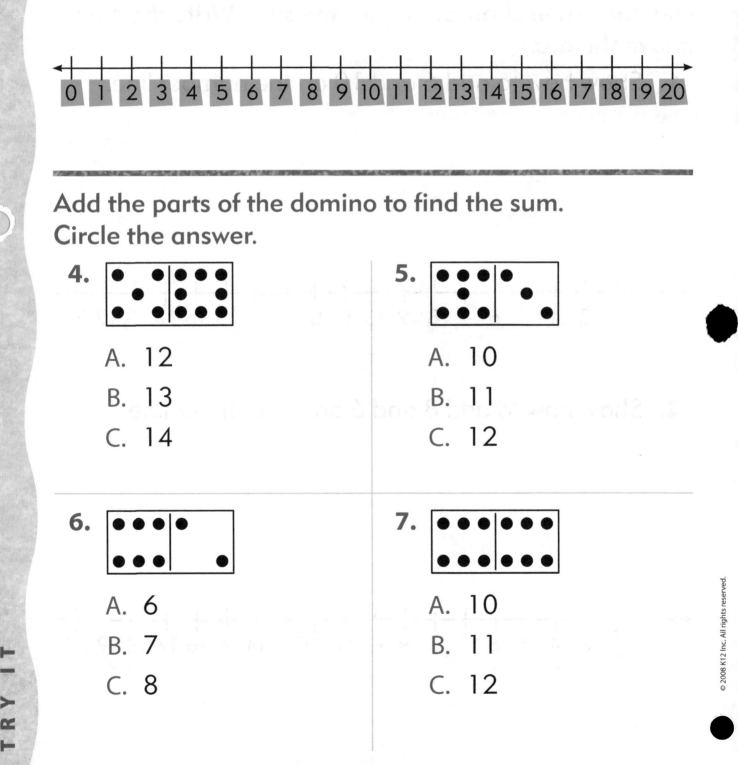

Add the parts of the domino to find the sum.
Circle the answer.

4.

A. 12

B. 13

C. 14

5.

A. 10

B. 11

C. 12

6.

A. 6

B. 7

C. 8

7.

A. 10

B. 11

C. 12

TRY IT

INTRODUCTION TO ADDITION

ADD WITH MODELS

Add with Models
Sketch with Models

Choose a domino. Make a drawing to show the numbers on the domino. Use dots, lines, or X's to make your drawing. Find the sum, and write it on the line.

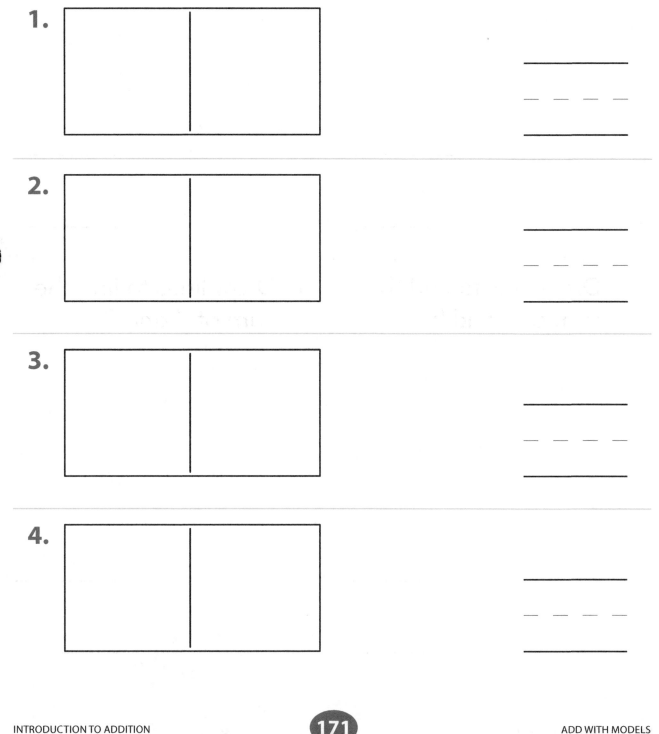

1.

2.

3.

4.

LEARN

Make a drawing to add. Write the sum on the line.

5. Draw circles to find the sum of 2 and 9.

_____
\- \- \- \-
_____

6. Draw squares to find the sum of 8 and 4.

_____
\- \- \- \-
_____

7. Draw dots to find the sum of 5 and 5.

_____
\- \- \- \-
_____

8. Draw lines to find the sum of 7 and 9.

_____
\- \- \- \-
_____

Add with Models

Sketch to Solve

Use circle blocks to show each problem. Then make drawings of your blocks. Circle the sum.

1. Add 5 and 2.
   A. 5
   B. 6
   C. 7

2. Add 4 and 8.
   A. 12
   B. 13
   C. 14

3. Add 6 and 3.
   A. 7
   B. 8
   C. 9

4. Add 5 and 5.
   A. 10
   B. 9
   C. 8

TRY IT

Use circle blocks to show each problem. Then make drawings of your blocks. Write the sum.

5. Add 9 and 8.

_____
_ _ _ _
_____

6. Add 10 and 8.

_____
_ _ _ _
_____

7. Add 7 and 2.

_____
_ _ _ _
_____

TRY IT

Use Sketches to Add

Use Sketches to Add Groups

Draw a large circle around the two groups to show combining. Then write the sum in your large circle.

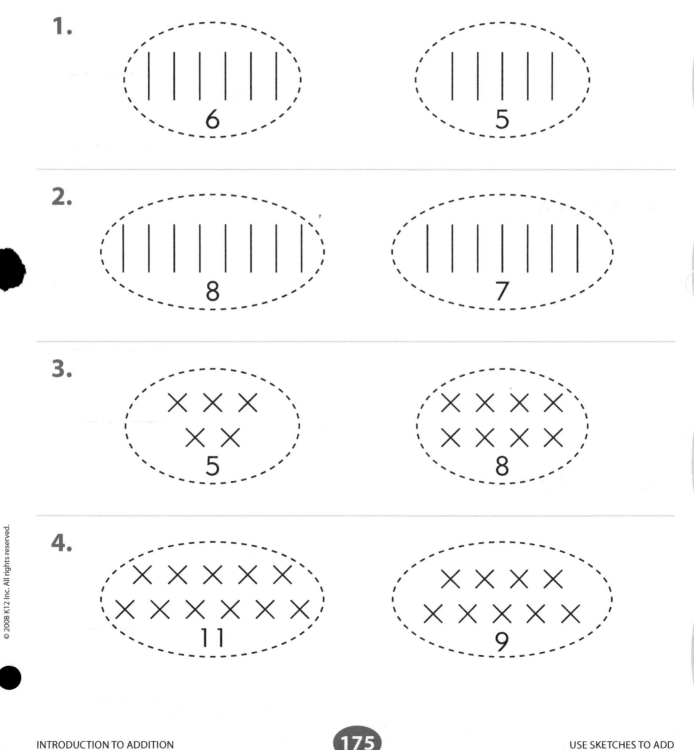

1.

6   5

2.

8   7

3.

5   8

4.

11   9

T R Y   I T

Draw pictures to show how to add the numbers.
Draw a large circle around your pictures to show
combining. Write the sum.

5. 7 and 3

_____
— — — —
_____

6. 4 and 4

_____
— — — —
_____

7. 6 and 3

_____
— — — —
_____

TRY IT

Unit Review

Checkpoint Practice

For Problems 1 and 2, use circle blocks.

1. Show a group of 5 blocks and a group of 11 blocks. Count. How many blocks are there? Circle the sum.

   A. 15   B. 16   C. 17

2. Use blocks to add 12 and 1. Circle the sum.

   A. 11   B. 12   C. 13

3. Draw a picture to find the sum of 8 and 3. Write the sum. _____

Use the number line to add. Show your work.

4. Show how to add 9 and 4 on the number line.

```
  0  1  2  3  4  5  6  7  8  9 10 11 12 13 14 15 16 17 18 19 20
```

5. Show how to add 4 and 9 on the number line.

```
  0  1  2  3  4  5  6  7  8  9 10 11 12 13 14 15 16 17 18 19 20
```

Did adding in a different order change the sum?
Circle Yes or No.

A. Yes   B. No

Read the problem and follow the directions.

6. You have 5 red apples and 12 green apples. Draw a picture to show how you would add all the apples.

Read the problem and circle the answer.

7. Look at the bees. You can count the bees in the circle and then count the bees in the square. If you count the bees in the square before you count the bees in the circle, will the sum change? Circle Yes or No.

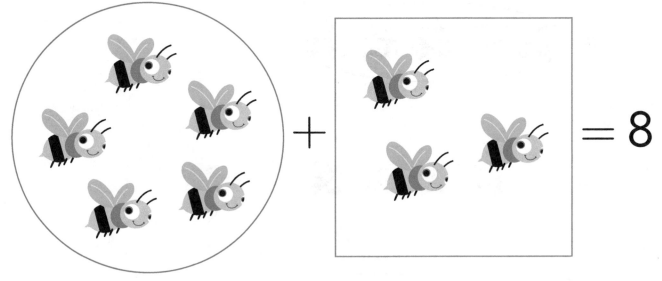

A. Yes   B. No

UNIT REVIEW

8. Does the model show how to add 3 and 2?

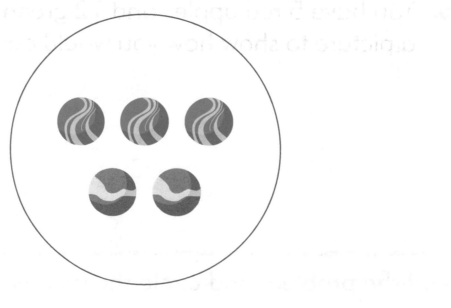

A. Yes   B. No

9. Which shows how to add 2 and 3?

A.

B.

C.

UNIT REVIEW

Addition Problem Solving

Snack on Story Problems

Use circles to solve each problem. Write the sum.

1. Tim has 4 pretzels.
Jake has 1 pretzel.

How many pretzels do they
have in all?   _____ pretzels

---

2. Matthew has 3 cheese sticks.
Sam has 1 cheese stick.

How many cheese sticks do
they have altogether?   _____ cheese sticks

---

3. Lisa has 6 crackers.
Roni has 2 crackers.

How many crackers do they
have altogether?   _____ crackers

---

4. Allie has 5 apple slices.
Henry has 1 apple slice.

How many apple slices do they
have in all?   _____ apple slices

T R Y   I T

Use circles to solve each problem. Write the sum.

5. Dan has 8 marbles.
Kim has 2 marbles.

How many marbles do they
have in all? _____ marbles

6. Isabel has 3 marbles.
Mellie has 1 marble.

How many marbles do they
have in all? _____ marbles

7. Spot the dog buried 6 bones.
Tiger the dog buried 2 bones.

How many bones did they
bury in all? _____ bones

8. Janie washed 4 cars.
Sally washed 2 cars.

How many cars did they
wash in all? _____ cars

9. Joely rode her bike 5 miles.
Claire rode her bike 2 miles.

How many miles did they ride
in all? _____ miles

TRY IT

Addition Story Problems

Sketch to Solve

Read each problem. Complete the sketch to solve each problem. Write the sum.

1. Alexander picked 6 yellow ears of corn. He also picked 4 white ears of corn.

   How many ears of corn did Alexander pick in all?

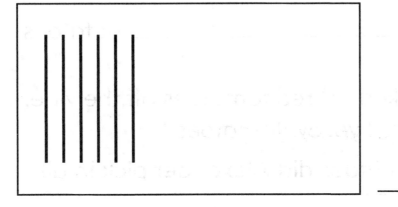

_____ ears of corn

2. Alexander saw 9 orange caterpillars in the garden. He also saw 5 brown caterpillars.

   How many caterpillars did Alexander see?

_____ caterpillars

LEARN

Read each problem. Use sketches to solve each problem. Write the sum.

3. Alexander dug 8 white potatoes from the garden. He also dug 7 red potatoes.

How many potatoes did Alexander dig in all from the garden?

_____ potatoes

4. Alexander picked 10 red tomatoes off the vine. He also picked 2 yellow tomatoes.

How many tomatoes did Alexander pick in all?

_____ tomatoes

5. Alexander saw 6 beetles. He also saw 3 spiders.

How many bugs did Alexander see altogether?

_____ bugs

LEARN

Name: _____

Addition Story Problems
Model It or Sketch It

Use cubes to solve each problem. Write the sum.

1. There are 4 red onions in the basket.
   There are 5 yellow onions in the basket.

   How many onions are there in all?

   _____ onions

2. There are 8 green apples in the bowl.
   There are 9 red apples in the bowl.

   How many apples in all are there? _____ apples

   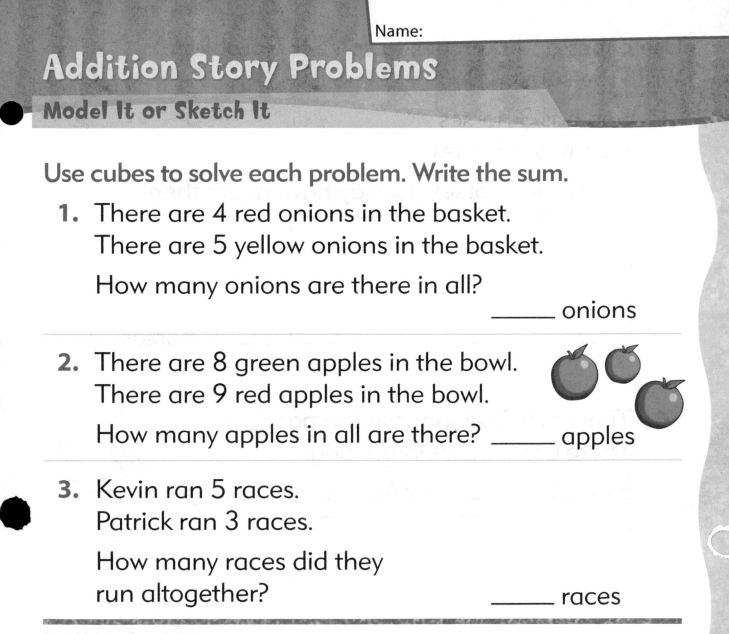

3. Kevin ran 5 races.
   Patrick ran 3 races.

   How many races did they
   run altogether?

   _____ races

Use cubes and sketches to solve the problem.
Write the sum.

4. Alexander picked 7 strawberries.
   He also picked 7 blackberries.

   How many berries did Alexander pick in all?

   _____ berries

TRY IT

Use cubes and sketches to solve the problem.
Write the sum.

5. Bob has 3 horses
Fran has 2 horses.

How many horses do they have altogether?

_____ horses

6. There are 2 bananas in the bag.
There are 6 pears in the bag.

How many pieces of fruit are in the bag?

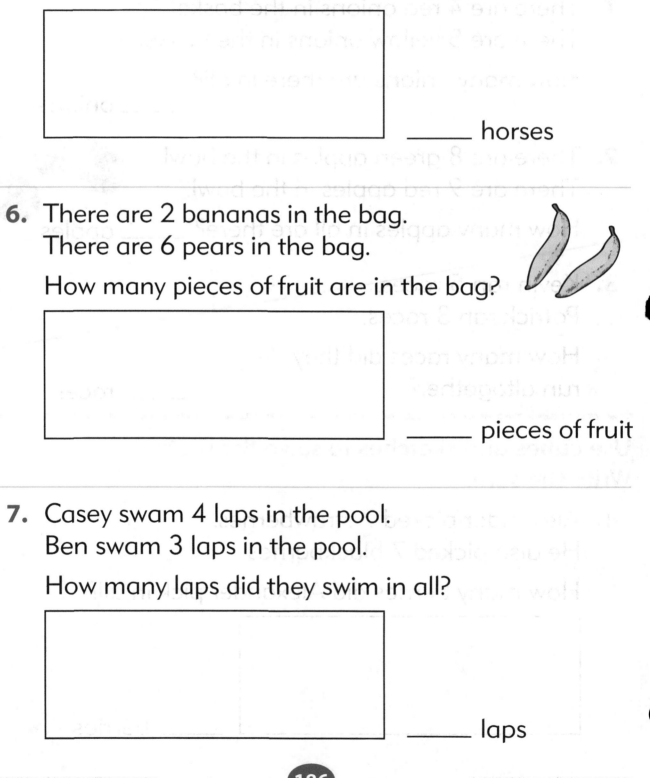

_____ pieces of fruit

7. Casey swam 4 laps in the pool.
Ben swam 3 laps in the pool.

How many laps did they swim in all?

_____ laps

TRY IT

Explain Addition Solutions

My Story Problems

Look at the pictures. Fill in the blanks to write an addition story problem about the pictures. Then solve it.

1.

_____ has _____ bananas.

_____ has _____ bananas.

How many bananas do they have in all?

2.

_____ has _____ water bottles.

_____ has _____ water bottles.

How many water bottles do they have in all?

_____ water bottles

L E A R N

Look at the pictures. Fill in the blanks to write an addition story problem about the pictures. Then solve it.

3.

_____ has _____ basketballs.

_____ has _____ baseballs.

How many balls do they have in all?

_____ balls

4. Look at the numbers. Tell an addition story problem by using the numbers. Then use sketches to solve it.

3	7

5. Make up your own addition story problem. Then solve it.

Think: What are the numbers?
What are the objects?

Explain Addition Solutions

Create Problems and Solve

Tell an addition story problem by using the two numbers.
Make sketches to show how to solve the problem.
Then explain how to solve the problem, and solve it.

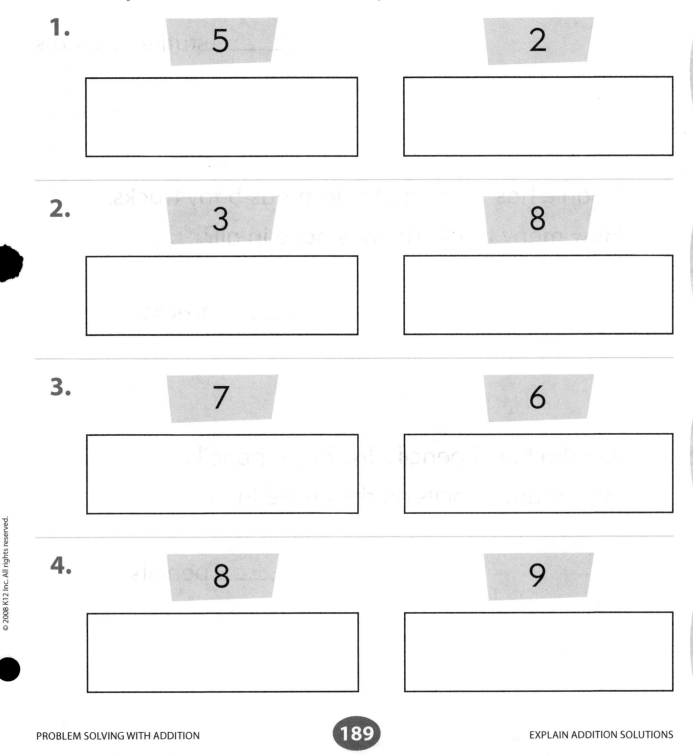

1. 5 2

2. 3 8

3. 7 6

4. 8 9

TRY IT

Use the circles to model each problem. Then solve the problem, and write the answer on the line.

5. Mona has 6 small stuffed animals.
   She has 4 large stuffed animals.
   How many stuffed animals does she have in all?

   _____ stuffed animals

6. Charlie has 3 toy trucks. Tom has 5 toy trucks.
   How many trucks do they have in all?

   _____ trucks

7. Kendra has 5 pencils. Iris has 4 pencils.
   How many pencils do they have in all?

   _____ pencils

Combine to Find Totals

Toy Problems

Use the Part-Part-Total Sheet and cubes to solve
each problem. Then write the answer on the line.

1. Winnie has 6 dominoes.
   Serena has 7 dominoes.

   How many dominoes do Winnie and
   Serena have in all?   _____ dominoes

2. There are 3 black checkers on the board.
   There are 6 red checkers on the board.

   How many checkers are on
   the board?   _____ checkers

3. Serena has 4 jacks.
   Winnie has 8 jacks.

   How many jacks do Winnie and
   Serena have altogether?   _____ jacks

4. There are 5 black cards in Winnie's hand.
   There are 9 red cards in Winnie's hand.

   How many cards are in Winnie's hand?

                                          _____ cards

T R Y   I T

Use the Part-Part-Total Sheet and cubes to solve each problem. Then circle the answer.

5. Pedro has 14 books.
   Shay has 6 books.

   How many do they have altogether?

   A. 8   B. 20   C. 16

6. A pet store has 12 hamsters in one habitat and 7 hamsters in another habitat.

   How many hamsters are there in the two habitats?

   A. 19   B. 15   C. 4

7. A cat ate 8 treats.
   A dog ate 7 treats.

   How many treats did they eat altogether?

   A. 14   B. 15   C. 1

8. The Best Berry Farm baked 10 apple pies.
   The farm also baked 3 peach pies.

   How many pies did the farm bake in all?

   A. 7   B. 8   C. 13

TRY IT

Recognize Combine Problems
Same-Number Problems

Use the Part-Part-Total Sheet and cubes to solve each problem. Write the total.

1. Paige ate 6 strawberries.
   Erin ate 8 strawberries.

   How many strawberries did they eat altogether?

   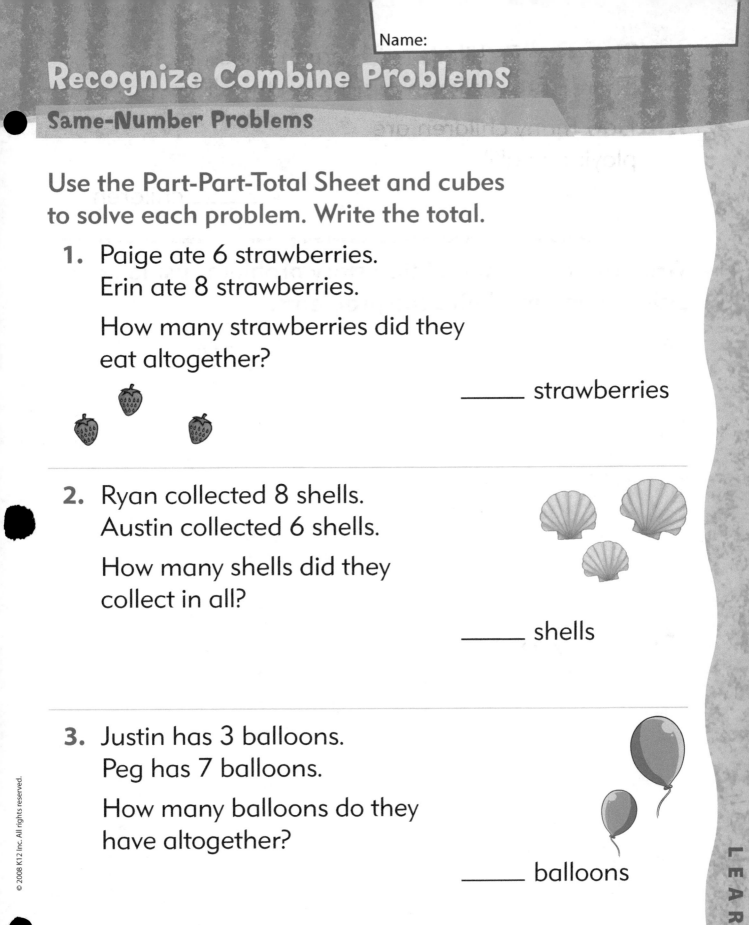

   _____ strawberries

2. Ryan collected 8 shells.
   Austin collected 6 shells.

   How many shells did they collect in all?

   _____ shells

3. Justin has 3 balloons.
   Peg has 7 balloons.

   How many balloons do they have altogether?

   _____ balloons

L E A R N

4. There are 7 children playing on the swings.
There are 3 children playing on the slides.

How many children are
playing in all?

_____ children

Write two different addition story problems using each
pair of numbers. Solve the problems.

5.

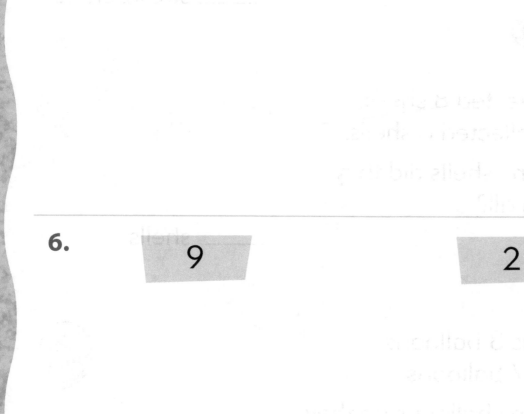

5   7

6.

9   2

Recognize Combine Problems

Snack-Time Problems

Read the problem. Can you use the Part-Part-Total Sheet to solve it? Circle Yes or No. If you circle Yes, solve the problem and write the answer.

1. Emily has 7 carrots. Sarah has 8 carrots.

   How many carrots do they have in all?

   Can you use the Part-Part-Total Sheet to solve the problem?

   A. Yes   B. No   _____ carrots

2. Adam ate 9 grapes. Ray ate 8 grapes.

   How many more grapes did Adam eat?

   Can you use the Part-Part-Total Sheet to solve the problem?

   A. Yes   B. No   _____ grapes

3. Kim has 5 crackers. Levi has 10 crackers.

   How many more crackers does Levi have than Kim?

   Can you use the Part-Part-Total Sheet to solve the problem?

   A. Yes   B. No   _____ crackers

TRY IT

4. Mandy ate 8 pretzel sticks. Ben ate 4 pretzel sticks. How many pretzel sticks in all did they eat?

Can you use the Part-Part-Total Sheet to solve the problem?

A. Yes   B. No   _____ pretzel sticks

5. David has 4 slices of cheese. Tom has 9 slices of cheese. How many slices of cheese do they have altogether?

Can you use the Part-Part-Total Sheet to solve the problem?

A. Yes   B. No   _____ slices of cheese

Read each problem and circle the answer.

6. What can you do to solve this problem?
There are 10 crackers in the bowl and 3 on the plate.

How many crackers are there altogether?

A. Put 10 and 3 together.

B. Take 3 away from 10.

7. What can you do to solve this problem?
Jim has 11 blocks. Lisa has 8 blocks.

How many blocks do they have in all?

A. Compare 11 and 8.

B. Add 11 and 8.

Estimate Sums Through 20

Estimate Sums of Story Problems

Estimate each sum. Write the answers.

1. Bob has 6 apples.

   Tom has 3 apples.

   About how many apples do
   Bob and Tom have in all?

   Think: Is 6 closer to 5 or 10?   about _____

   Think: Is 3 closer to 0 or 5?   about _____

   Think: Estimate the sum.   about _____

2. Megan collected 4 eggs.

   Sarah collected 9 eggs.

   About how many eggs did
   Megan and Sarah collect in all?

   Think: Is 4 closer to 5 or 10?   about _____

   Think: Is 9 closer to 5 or 10?   about _____

   Think: Estimate the sum.   about _____

LEARN

3. Gina has 12 buttons.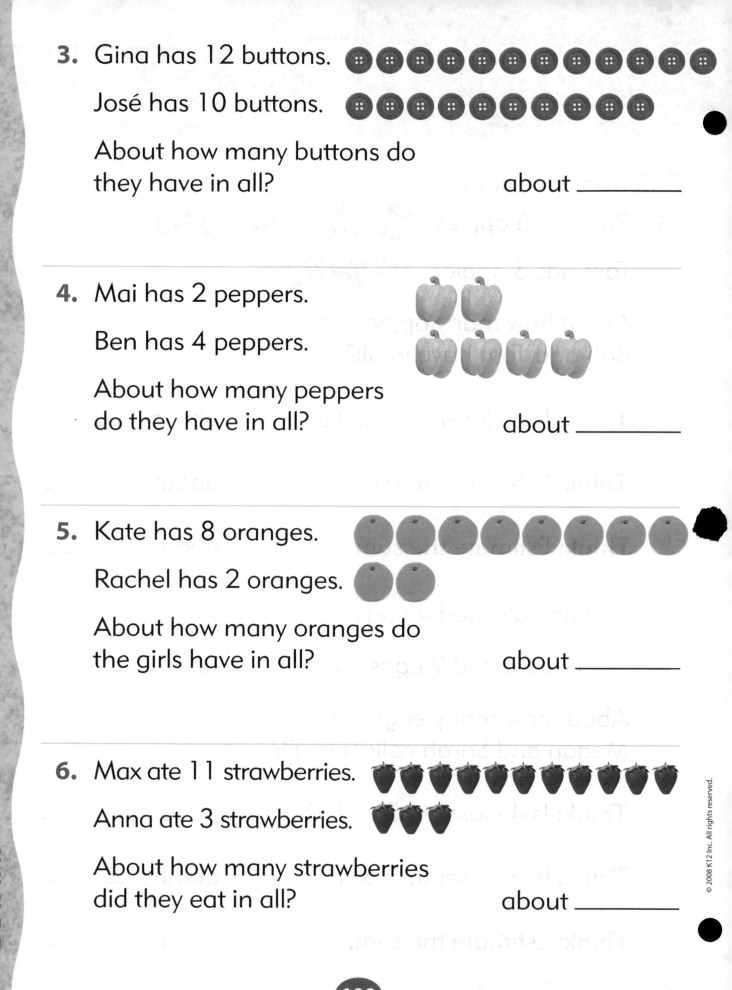

José has 10 buttons.

About how many buttons do
they have in all?

about _____

4. Mai has 2 peppers.

Ben has 4 peppers.

About how many peppers
do they have in all?

about _____

5. Kate has 8 oranges.

Rachel has 2 oranges.

About how many oranges do
the girls have in all?

about _____

6. Max ate 11 strawberries.

Anna ate 3 strawberries.

About how many strawberries
did they eat in all?

about _____

L E A R N

Estimate Sums Through 20

Estimate Sums

Estimate each number. Then write the answers. Circle the estimate.

1. Estimate the sum of 11 and 3.

Think: Is 11 closer to 5 or 10?   about _____

Think: Is 3 closer to 5 or 10?   about _____

Think: Estimate the sum.

A. about 10   B. about 15   C. about 20

---

2. Estimate the sum of 11 and 9.

Think: Is 9 closer to 5 or 10?   about _____

Think: Is 11 closer to 5 or 10?   about _____

Think: Estimate the sum.

A. about 10   B. about 15   C. about 20

---

3. Estimate the sum of 3 pears and 1 pear.

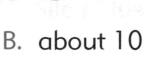

A. about 5   B. about 10   C. about 15

TRY IT

4. Estimate the sum of 3 lemons and 6 lemons.

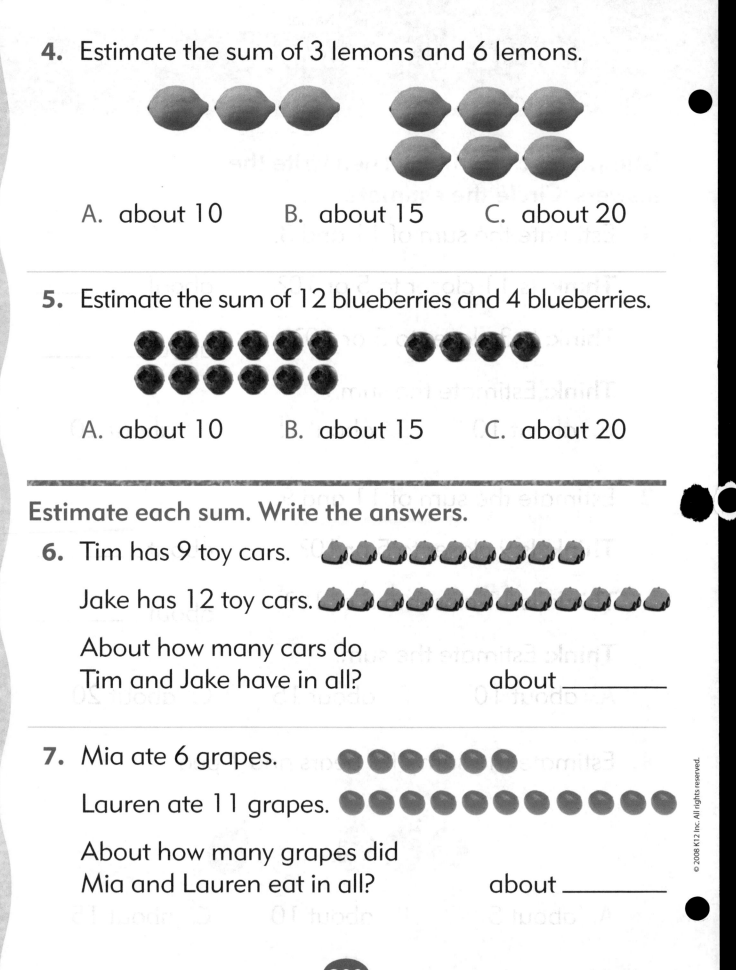

  A. about 10   B. about 15   C. about 20

5. Estimate the sum of 12 blueberries and 4 blueberries.

  A. about 10   B. about 15   C. about 20

Estimate each sum. Write the answers.

6. Tim has 9 toy cars.

Jake has 12 toy cars.

About how many cars do
Tim and Jake have in all?   about _____

7. Mia ate 6 grapes.

Lauren ate 11 grapes.

About how many grapes did
Mia and Lauren eat in all?   about _____

Check the Accuracy of Calculations

Check Problems

Use cubes to check each problem. Circle the problem that has a correct answer.

1. Which math problem is correct?

    A. 4 cups and 2 cups makes 7 cups.

    B. 8 cups and 3 cups makes 12 cups.

    C. 9 cups and 5 cups makes 14 cups.

2. Which math problem is correct?

    A. 2 plates and 3 plates makes 5 plates.

    B. 6 plates and 7 plates makes 14 plates.

    C. 8 plates and 9 plates makes 18 plates.

L E A R N

3. Which math problem is correct? Use cubes to show how you know your answer is correct.

    A. 6 spoons and 3 spoons makes 10 spoons.

    B. 7 spoons and 7 spoons makes 15 spoons.

    C. 9 spoons and 10 spoons makes 19 spoons.

4. Which math problem is correct?

    A. 1 bowl and 6 bowls makes 7 bowls.

    B. 8 bowls and 5 bowls makes 11 bowls.

    C. 6 bowls and 4 bowls makes 9 bowls.

LEARN

Check the Accuracy of Calculations

For Problems 1 and 2, use cubes to check each problem. Circle the problem that has a correct answer.

1. Which math problem is correct?

   A. 1 orange and 4 oranges makes 6 oranges.

   B. 3 oranges and 5 oranges makes 9 oranges.

   C. 6 oranges and 6 oranges makes 12 oranges.

2. Which math problem is correct?

   A. 5 apples and 5 apples makes 11 apples.

   B. 7 apples and 8 apples makes 16 apples.

   C. 9 apples and 4 apples makes 13 apples.

3. Which math problem is correct? Make a sketch to show how you know the answer is correct.

   A. 5 soccer balls and 3 soccer balls makes 8 soccer balls.

   B. 4 soccer balls and 5 soccer balls makes 7 soccer balls.

   C. 3 soccer balls and 8 soccer balls makes 9 soccer balls.

T R Y I T

Use cubes to check the problem. Circle the answer.

4. Alexander did this math problem. 5 pencils and 7 pencils makes 13 pencils. Is Alexander correct?

    A. Yes

    B. No

5. Serena did this math problem. 9 baseballs and 9 baseballs makes 17 baseballs. Is Serena correct?

    A. Yes

    B. No

Make a sketch to check the problem. Explain how to use the sketch to check. Circle the answer.

6. Alexander did this math problem. 9 bananas and 10 bananas makes 18 bananas. Is Alexander correct?

    A. Yes

    B. No

7. Serena did this math problem. 7 peaches and 7 peaches makes 14 peaches. Is Serena correct?

    A. Yes

    B. No

TRY IT

For Problems 1 and 2, use the Part-Part-Total
Sheet and cubes to solve. Write the answer.

1. Patrick has 3 paper airplanes.
    Ricky has 2 paper airplanes.

    How many paper airplanes
    do they have in all?   _____ paper airplanes

2. Amber collected 7 pinecones.
    Nicole collected 9 pinecones.

    How many pinecones did
    they collect altogether?   _____ pinecones

Circle the best estimate.

3. Estimate the sum of 6 and 14.

    A. about 5   B. about 10
    C. about 15   D. about 20

4. Estimate the sum of 1 and 5.

    A. about 5   B. about 10
    C. about 15   D. about 20

Read the problem and write the answer.

5. Use cubes to solve the story problem.

Sheila has 8 pink flowers.
She has 5 blue flowers.

How many flowers does she have in all? _____ flowers

Explain how you used the cubes
to find out how many flowers Sheila has in all.

---

6. Jane put 4 beads on her necklace.
Terry put 3 beads on her necklace.

How many beads did they put on
the necklaces in all?   _____ beads

Read the problem and circle the answer.

7. Bror solved this math problem.

5 cars and 6 cars equals 12 cars.

Use cubes to check his work. Is Bror correct?

A. Yes   B. No

---

8. Alexander solved this math problem.

8 baseballs and 7 baseballs equals 14 baseballs.

Use a sketch to check his work.
Is Alexander correct?

A. Yes   B. No

UNIT REVIEW

Name:

Take Away to Subtract

Take Away Cubes

Use cubes to model the problem.

1. 6 take away 5

2. 13 take away 6

3. 13 take away 4

TRY IT

4. 9 take away 3

Tell how many cubes are left.

5. Show 10 cubes.
Take away 8.

How many cubes are left?

6. Show 16 cubes.
Take away 7.

How many cubes are left?

7. Show 10 cubes.
Take away 4.

How many cubes are left?

TRY IT

Name:

Subtract with Objects
Subtract 1 or Subtract 2

Use circles to show the subtraction problem.
Write how many are left.

1. 8 take away 1 is _____
   - - - - - - -
   _____.

2. 10 take away 1 is _____
   - - - - - - -
   _____.

3. 17 take away 1 is _____
   - - - - - - -
   _____.

4. 3 take away 2 is _____
   - - - - - - -
   _____.

5. 12 take away 2 is _____
   - - - - - - -
   _____.

6. 19 take away 2 is _____
   - - - - - - -
   _____.

© K12 Inc. All rights reserved.

T R Y   I T

INTRODUCTION TO SUBTRACTION   209   SUBTRACT WITH OBJECTS

7. 20 take away 2 is _____

_ _ _ _ _ _ _ _

_____ .

8. 9 take away 1 is _____

_ _ _ _ _ _ _ _

_____ .

9. 15 take away 2 is _____

_ _ _ _ _ _ _ _

_____ .

10. Use circles to show how to subtract 2 from 10.

_____

_ _ _ _ _ _ _

_____

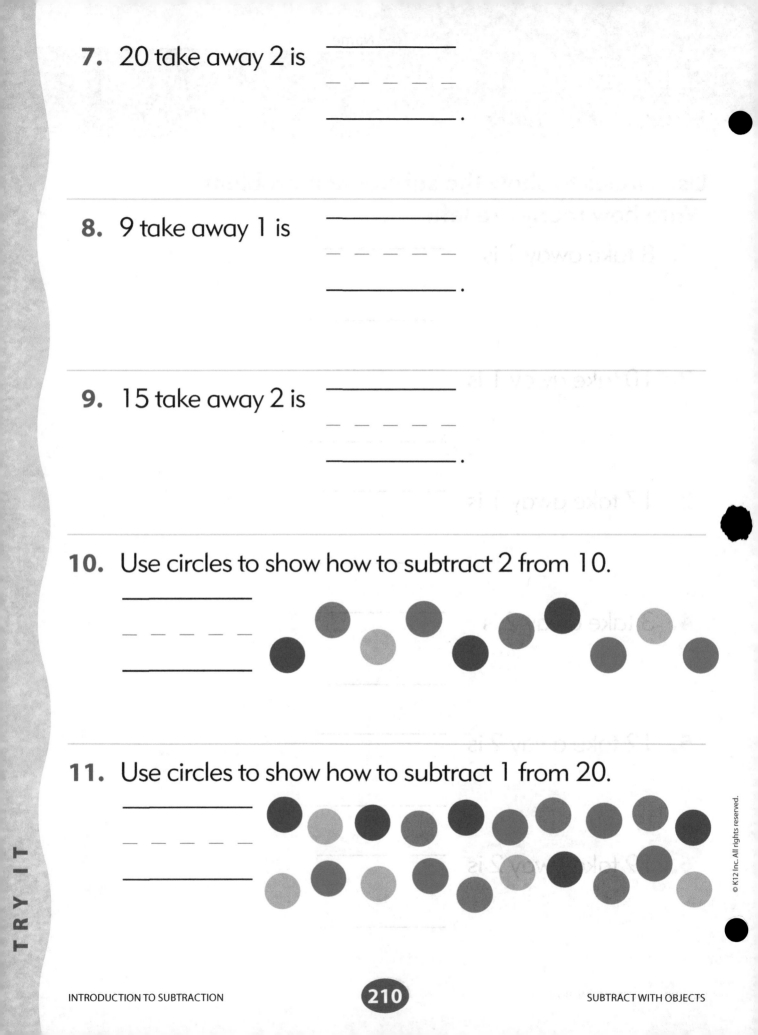

11. Use circles to show how to subtract 1 from 20.

_____

_ _ _ _ _ _ _

_____

TRY IT

Model Subtraction

Different Ways to Subtract

Use cubes to show the subtraction problem.
Write how many are left.

1. 14 take away 6 is _____.   **2.** 17 take away 8 is _____.

Use the number line to show the subtraction
problem. Write how many are left.

3. 9 take away 6 is _____.

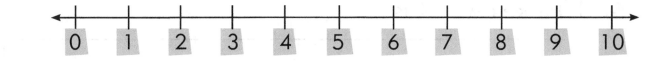

4. 6 take away 4 is _____.

T R Y I T

Use sketches to show the subtraction problem. Write how many are left.

5. 12 take away 5 is _____.

6. 10 take away 4 is _____.

TRY IT

Subtract with Pictures

Solve with Pictures

Count the objects. Cross out the number of objects to be taken away. Write how many are left.

1. 15 take away 8 is _____.

2. 12 take away 7 is _____.

3. 17 take away 9 is _____.

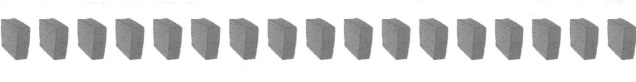

4. 11 take away 5 is _____.

TRY IT

Use circles to show the problem.
Write how many are left.

5. 15 take away 8 _____

6. 19 take away 5 _____

7. 13 take away 7 _____

8. 20 take away 14 _____

9. 14 take away 5 _____

TRY IT

Estimate and Check Differences

Check Calculations

Name: _____

Use circles to check the answer.
Circle the answer.

1. Serena used circles to solve a subtraction word problem.

She says 17 socks take away 9 socks is 9 socks.

Is Serena correct?

A. Yes   B. No

2. Alexander used circles to solve a subtraction word problem.

He says 10 stamps take away 5 stamps is 5 stamps.

Is Alexander correct?

A. Yes   B. No

3. Serena used circles to solve a subtraction word problem.

She says 15 stones take away 7 stones is 8 stones.

Is Serena correct?

A. Yes   B. No

LEARN

4. Alexander used circles to solve a subtraction word problem.
He says 8 crayons take away 4 crayons is 5 crayons.

Is Alexander correct?

A. Yes   B. No

Use sketches to check the answer.
Circle the answer.

5. Alexander used a sketch to solve a subtraction word problem.
He says 13 books take away 5 books is 7 books.

Is Alexander correct?

A. Yes   B. No

---

6. Serena used a sketch to solve a subtraction word problem.
She says 9 shells take away 5 shells is 5 shells.

Is Serena correct?

A. Yes   B. No

Estimate and Check Differences

Estimate and Check

Find the estimate.

1. Estimate the difference if you take away 3 from 9.

Is 9 closer to 5 or 10? _____

Is 3 closer to 5 or 10? _____

Estimate: What is the difference?
9 take away 3 is about _____.

2. Estimate the difference if you take away 8 from 19.

Is 19 closer to 15 or 20? _____

Is 8 closer to 5 or 10? _____

Estimate: What is the difference?
19 take away 8 is about _____.

© K12 Inc. All rights reserved.

TRY IT

INTRODUCTION TO SUBTRACTION

217

ESTIMATE AND CHECK DIFFERENCES

3. 14 take away 8 is about _____.

4. 16 take away 4 is about _____.

5. About how many is 14 take away 4? _____

6. You had 19 stickers. You gave 4 stickers away.
About how many stickers do you have left?
Circle the answer.

    A. about 20   B. about 10   C. about 15

7. Estimate the difference.
19 take away 10 is about _____.

8. Estimate the difference.
15 take away 6 is about _____.

Decide whether the answer is correct or incorrect. Circle the answer.

9. Alexander did this math problem:
   9 plants take away 7 plants is 2 plants.

   Explain how to use a sketch to check his work.

   Is Alexander correct?

   A. Yes   B. No

---

10. Serena did this math problem:
    14 pebbles take away 5 pebbles is 8 pebbles.

    Explain how to use a sketch to check her work.

    Is Serena correct?

    A. Yes   B. No

---

11. Alexander did this math problem:
    12 stamps take away 3 stamps is 9 stamps.

    Explain how to use circles to check his work.

    Is Alexander correct?

    A. Yes   B. No

© K12 Inc. All rights reserved.

INTRODUCTION TO SUBTRACTION   219   ESTIMATE AND CHECK DIFFERENCES

12. Serena did this math problem:
16 socks take away 7 socks is 8 socks.

Explain how to use circles to check her work.

Is Serena correct?

A. Yes   B. No

13. Which math problem is incorrect?

A. 8 cats take away 4 cats is 4 cats.

B. 7 cats take away 1 cat is 6 cats.

C. 9 cats take away 3 cats is 7 cats.

14. Johnny did this math problem:
15 dogs take away 3 dogs is 13 dogs.

Check his work by using the dogs shown.

Is Johnny correct?

A. Yes   B. No

15. Winnie solved this problem:
10 birds take away 2 birds is 8 birds.

Check her work by using the birds shown.

Is Winnie correct?

A. Yes   B. No

TRY IT

Name: _____

Use circles to model the subtraction problem.
Write how many are left.

1. 8 take away 6 is _____.

2. 13 take away 8 is _____.

3. Place 7 circles on the table.
Show how to subtract 3 circles.

7 take away 3 is _____.

4. Place 8 circles on the table.
Show how to subtract 6 circles.

8 take away 6 is _____.

5. Subtract 4 from 12.
How many are left?

_____

6. Subtract 5 from 14.
How many are left?

_____

Find the estimate. Circle the answer.

7. 19 take away 8 is about _____.

    A. 5   B. 10   C. 15

8. 18 take away 9 is about _____.

    A. 20   B. 10   C. 5

9. About how many is 16 take away 9?

    A. about 15   B. about 10   C. about 5

Use sketches to solve the problem.

10. 10 take away 4 is _____.

UNIT REVIEW

Use sketches or circles to solve the problem.
Circle the answer.

11. Serena did this math problem:
11 bracelets take away 4 bracelets is
7 bracelets.

Check Serena's work.

Is Serena correct?

A. Yes   B. No

12. Ron did this math problem:
9 monkeys take away 2 monkeys is
7 monkeys.

Check Ron's work.

Is Ron correct?

A. Yes   B. No

UNIT REVIEW

13. Winnie did this math problem:
18 kites take away 2 kites is 16 kites.

Check Winnie's work.

Is Winnie correct?

A. Yes   B. No

Sketch Subtraction Stories

Model and Sketch Stories

Use cubes to solve the problem.
Write the answer.

1. There were 10 tomatoes in a basket at the store. 7 tomatoes were sold.

   How many tomatoes are
   left in the basket?   _____ tomatoes

2. Alexander had 6 peaches.
   He ate 2 peaches.

   How many peaches does
   Alexander have left?   _____ peaches

Use cubes and sketches to solve the problem.
Write the answer.

3. John had 8 grapes.
   He ate 3 grapes.

   How many grapes does
   John have left?   _____ grapes

T R Y   I T

Use sketches to solve problem.
Write the answer.

4. Alexander picked 9 apples.
He gave 8 of them to his family.

How many apples does
Alexander have left?   _____ apples

---

5. The baker had 10 muffins.
She sold 10 muffins.

How many muffins does
the baker have left?   _____ muffins

---

6. A farmer had 7 sheep.
He sold 2 of them.

How many sheep does
the farmer have left?   _____ sheep

TRY IT

Take-Away Stories

Story Problem Explanations

Name:

Tell about the steps.
Use cubes to solve the problem.

Example: Jill had 10 grapes.
She ate 6 grapes.

How many grapes does
Jill have left?   __4__ grapes

1. There were 8 postage stamps.
    Ken used 5 stamps on his letters.

    How many postage stamps
    are left?   _____ stamps

2. There were 4 turtles on the grass.
    Then 3 turtles went into the pond.

    How many turtles are left
    on the grass?   _____ turtles

3. There were 7 strawberries in a bowl.
    Tom ate 2 strawberries.

    How many strawberries
    are left in the bowl?   _____ strawberries

TRY IT

© K12 Inc. All rights reserved.

4. Mandy had 9 hats.
She sold 4 hats.

How many hats does she have left? _____ hats

Solve the problem. Write or circle the answer.

5. Mark had 7 carrots.
He ate 3 carrots at lunchtime.

How many carrots does Mark have left? _____ carrots

---

6. James had 8 trucks.
He gave 2 trucks to his sister.

How many trucks does James have now? _____ trucks

---

7. Therese made 6 pizzas.
5 pizzas got eaten.

How many pizzas does Therese have left? _____ pizzas

---

8. Javier made 9 paintings to sell at the fair.
He sold 8 of them.

How many paintings does Javier have left?

A. 1 B. 4 C. 17

---

9. Sophie had 6 blocks.
She gave 2 blocks to Molly.

How many blocks does Sophie have now? _____ blocks

Compare Take-Away and Combine

Add or Subtract?

Use the picture and your cubes to act out the problem. Then circle the way you found the answer.

1. There were 8 bees on a flower.
   5 more bees flew over.

   Now how many bees are on the flower?

   A. I put the parts together.

   B. I took away a part from the total.

TRY IT

2. Henry had a box of 12 crickets.
He gave 7 crickets to Sam.

Now how many crickets does Henry have?

A. I put the parts together.

B. I took away a part from the total.

3. There were 13 monkeys in a tree.
Then 4 monkeys jumped off the tree.

How many monkeys are left?

A. I combined 13 and 4.

B. I took away 4 from 13.

4. There were 7 toads in the pond.
Then 3 more toads jumped into the pond.

How many toads are in the pond altogether?

A. I combined 7 and 3.

B. I took away 3 from 7.

5. There were 9 butterflies in the garden.
Then 2 butterflies flew away.

How many butterflies are left in the garden?

A. I combined 9 and 2.

B. I took away 2 from 9.

Make Estimates and Check Answers

Check the answer to the problem by drawing a sketch. Then circle the answer.

1. Ron solved this subtraction story problem:
17 rockets take away 8 rockets is 10 rockets.

First, draw 17 lines.
Then cross out 8.

How many lines are not crossed out? _____

Is Ron's answer correct?

A. Yes   B. No

2. Serena solved this subtraction story problem:
10 rocks take away 3 rocks is 6 rocks.

Is Serena's answer correct?

A. Yes   B. No

Use circles or sketches to check the problem. Then circle the answer.

3. Serena solved this subtraction story problem: 13 books take away 7 books is 6 books.

Is Serena's answer correct?

A. Yes   B. No

4. Serena solved this subtraction story problem: 16 bookmarks take away 9 bookmarks is 8 bookmarks.

Is Serena's answer correct?

A. Yes   B. No

5. Alexander solved this subtraction story problem: 6 eggs take away 4 eggs is 3 eggs.

Is Alexander's answer correct?

A. Yes   B. No

6. Alexander solved this subtraction story problem: 15 beans take away 8 beans is 6 beans.

Is Alexander's answer correct?

A. Yes   B. No

LEARN

Make Estimates and Check Answers

Estimate and Check Answers

Use models or sketches to estimate or check the problem. Then circle the answer.

1. You had 19 baseball cards.
   You gave 6 baseball cards to a friend.

   About how many baseball cards do you have left?

   A. about 5   B. about 10   C. about 15

2. Maria saw 18 birds.
   Then 9 birds flew away.

   About how many birds are left?

   A. about 5   B. about 10   C. about 15

3. Rosa solved this subtraction story problem.
   18 blocks take away 9 blocks is 9 blocks.

   Is Rosa's answer correct?

   A. Yes   B. No

4. Winnie solved this subtraction story problem.
   14 marbles take away 6 marbles is 9 marbles.

   Is Winnie's answer correct?

   A. Yes   B. No

TRY IT

5. You had 18 crackers.
Your friend ate 9 of your crackers.
About how many crackers are left?

   A. about 20   B. about 10   C. about 0

6. You had 19 stamps.
You gave 4 stamps away.
About how many stamps do you have left?

   A. about 20   B. about 10   C. about 15

7. Which subtraction story problem is correct?

   A. 8 cookies take away 3 cookies is 4 cookies.

   B. 9 cookies take away 6 cookies is 3 cookies.

   C. 7 cookies take away 2 cookies is 6 cookies.

8. Which subtraction story problem is correct?

   A. 13 bananas take away 2 bananas is 11 bananas.

   B. 18 bananas take away 3 bananas is 14 bananas.

   C. 20 bananas take away 5 bananas is 16 bananas.

TRY IT

Unit Review

Use cubes or sketches to solve the problem.
Explain your answer.

1. There were 8 balloons in the sky.
   3 balloons popped.

   How many balloons are left
   in the sky?   _____ balloons

   ┌───┐
   │   │
   │   │
   │   │
   │   │
   └───┘

2. There were 5 people sitting at the table.
   Then 5 people got up and left.

   How many people are left at
   the table?   _____ people

   ┌───┐
   │   │
   │   │
   │   │
   │   │
   └───┘

UNIT REVIEW

Use cubes to solve the problem.
Explain your answer.

3. There were 14 bananas in the basket.
   Then 7 bananas were sold.

   How many bananas are left
   in the basket?   _____ bananas

4. Sydney has 9 rockets.
   His friend has 6 rockets.

   How many rockets do they
   have altogether?   _____ rockets

Use cubes to solve the problem.

5. Joan had 12 bananas.
   She used 4 to make banana bread.

   How many bananas does Joan
   have left?   _____ bananas

Read the problem. Circle the answer.

6. Ryan had 19 straws.
He gave 4 to some friends.

About how many straws does Ryan have left?

A. about 5   B. about 10   C. about 15

---

7. Jean has 15 bows.
She gives Susie 8 bows.

About how many bows does Jean have left?

A. about 5   B. about 10   C. about 15

---

8. Alexander solved this problem:
13 hats take away 5 hats is 7 hats.

Check Alexander's answer with cubes.

Is Alexander's answer correct?

A. Yes   B. No

UNIT REVIEW

9. Fred baked 9 mini pizzas.
He and his family ate 3 of them.

Which shows how many mini pizzas Fred has left?

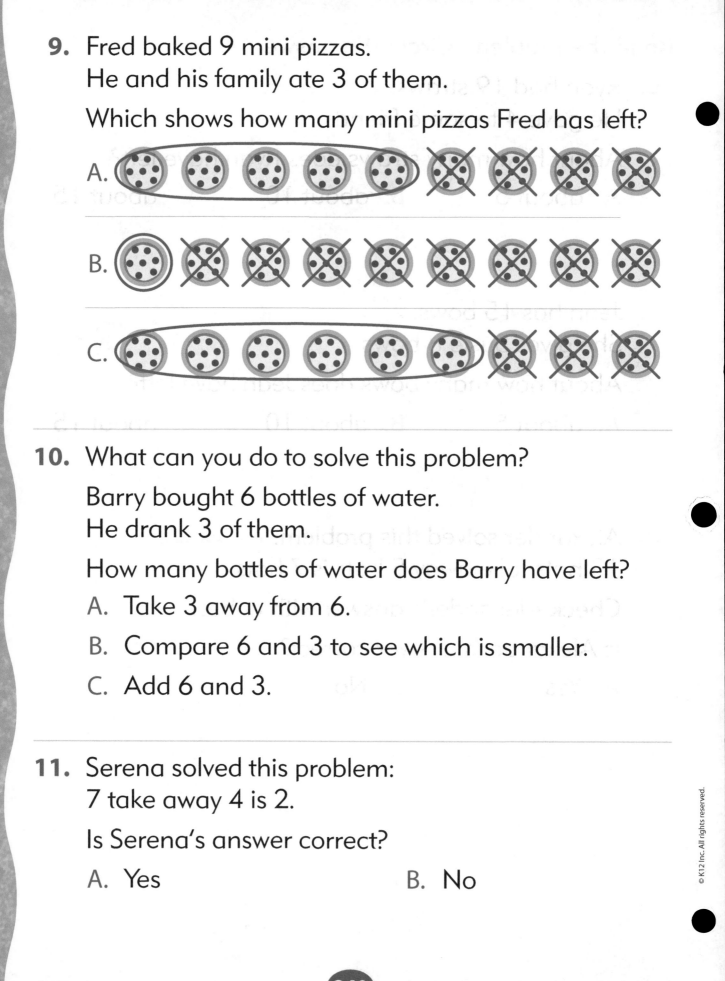

A.

B.

C.

10. What can you do to solve this problem?

Barry bought 6 bottles of water.
He drank 3 of them.

How many bottles of water does Barry have left?

A. Take 3 away from 6.

B. Compare 6 and 3 to see which is smaller.

C. Add 6 and 3.

11. Serena solved this problem:
7 take away 4 is 2.

Is Serena's answer correct?

A. Yes

B. No

Compare and Subtract
Pair Objects to Solve

Cut out the envelopes and stamps.

LEARN

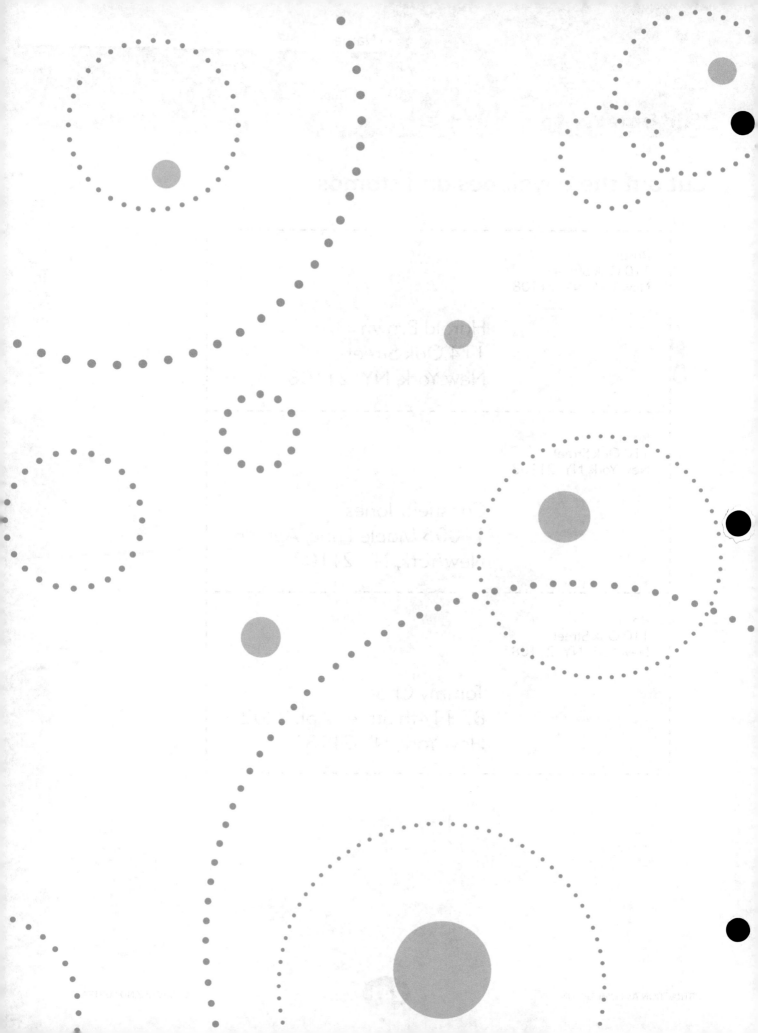

Rosa
110 Oak Street
New York, NY 21108

Sally Smith
223 Center Street
New York, NY 21162

Rosa
110 Oak Street
New York, NY 21108

Dan Estrada
85 Barter Street
New York, NY 21108

Rosa
110 Oak Street
New York, NY 21108

Amelia Bright
75 Ash Lane
New York, NY 21108

Rosa
110 Oak Street
New York, NY 21108

Madeline Dokes
8843 79th Street, Apt. B
New York, NY 21108

Rosa
110 Oak Street
New York, NY 21108

Susan Danforth
90 Birch Court
New York, NY 21181

LEARN

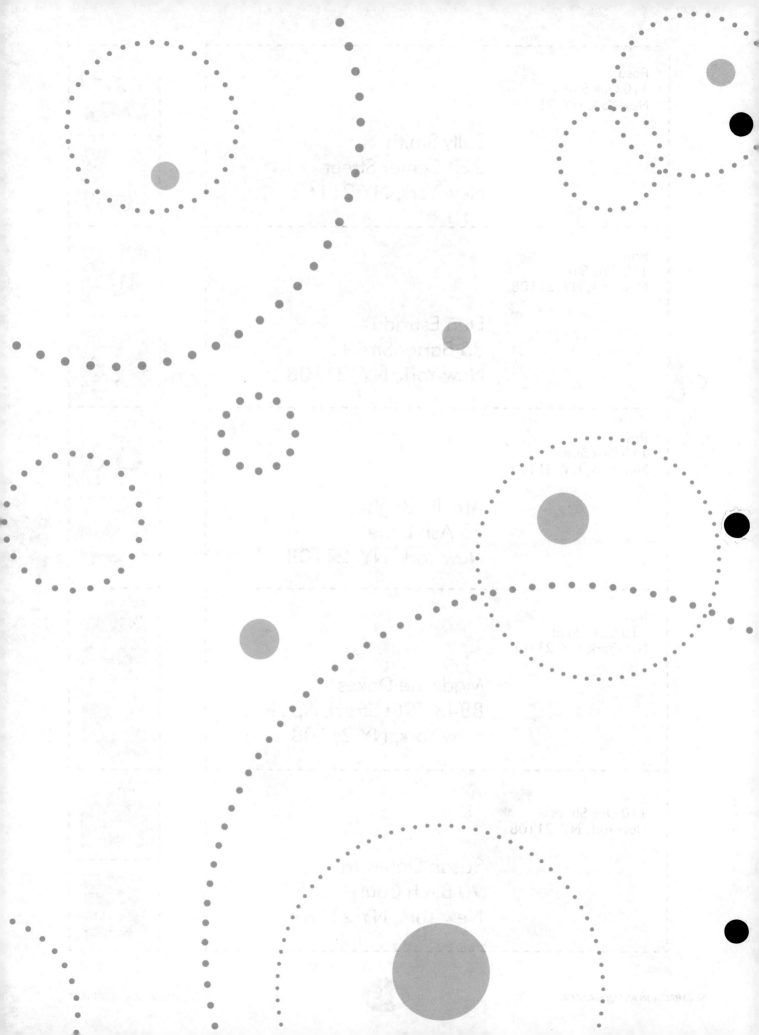

Compare and Subtract

Compare and Solve

Model and solve the problem.

1. 5 is how many more than 3?

5 is _____ more than 3.

2. 8 is how many more than 4?

8 is _____ more than 4.

3. 5 is how many more than 1?

5 is _____ more than 1.

4. 1 is how many fewer than 6?

1 is _____ fewer than 6.

5. 4 is how many fewer than 9?

4 is _____ fewer than 9.

T R Y   I T

6. 3 is how many fewer than 5?

3 is _____ fewer than 5.

7. 2 is how many fewer than 3?

2 is _____ fewer than 3.

8. 10 is how many more than 7?

10 is _____ more than 7.

TRY IT

Sketch Subtraction Problems
Compare Numbers

Draw a sketch to compare the numbers. Then write a subtraction sentence to compare the numbers.

1. 14 is how many more than 3?

[ ] minus [ ] is [ ] .

2. 15 is how many more than 3?

[ ] minus [ ] is [ ] .

L E A R N

3. 16 is how many more than 3?

[ ] minus [ ] is [ ] .

---

4. 7 is how many more than 5?

[ ] minus [ ] is [ ] .

LEARN

5. 2 is how many fewer than 9?

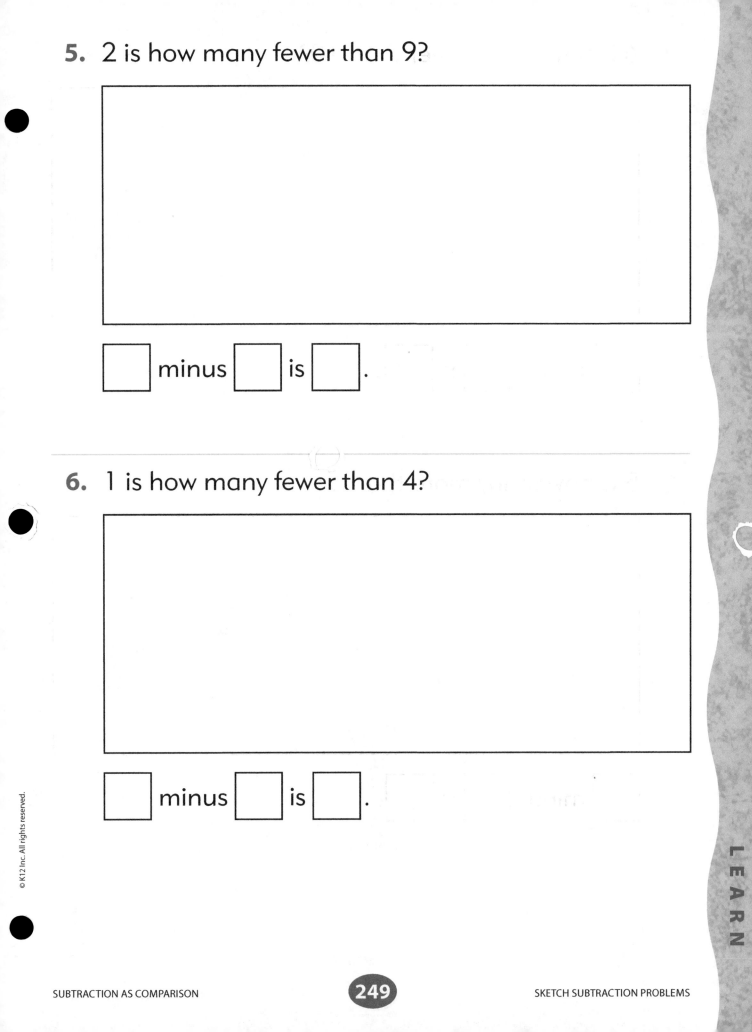

☐ minus ☐ is ☐ .

---

6. 1 is how many fewer than 4?

☐ minus ☐ is ☐ .

L E A R N

7. 6 is how many fewer than 10?

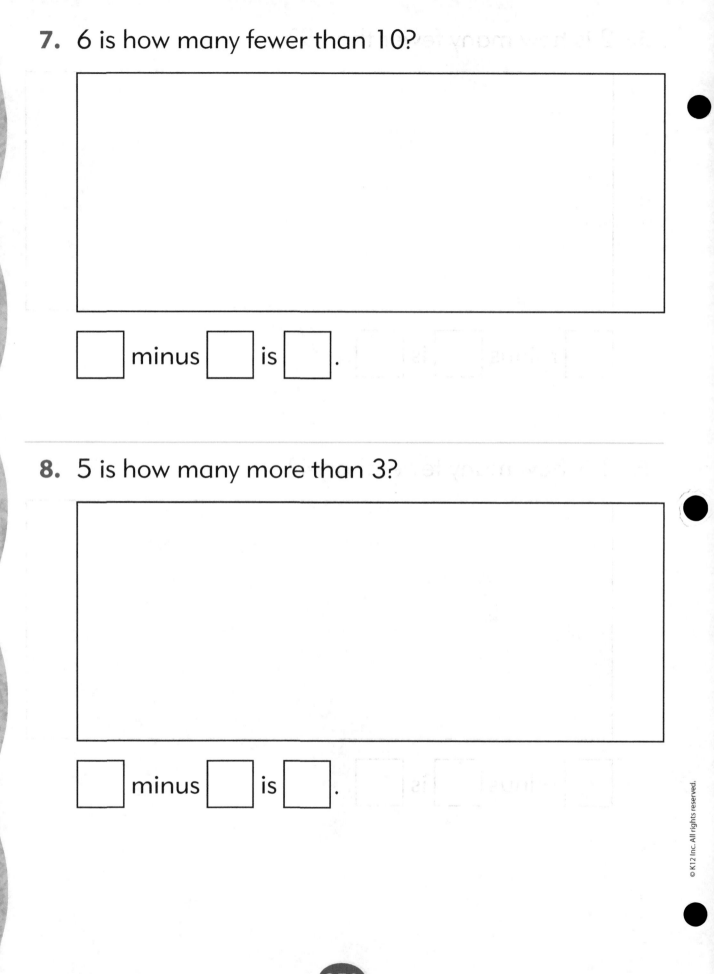

[ ] minus [ ] is [ ].

8. 5 is how many more than 3?

[ ] minus [ ] is [ ].

Sketch Subtraction Problems

Sketch and Solve

Draw a sketch to solve.

1. 14 is how many more than 4?

2. 18 is how many more than 9?

T R Y   I T

3. 2 is how many fewer than 8?

4. 5 is how many fewer than 16?

TRY IT

Draw a sketch and write a subtraction sentence.
Then complete the subtraction statement.

5. 9 is how many more than 2?

| |

☐ minus ☐ is ☐ .

9 is _____ more than 2.

6. 7 is how many more than 3?

| |

☐ minus ☐ is ☐ .

7 is _____ more than 3.

TRY IT

7. 1 is how many fewer than 2?

[ ] minus [ ] is [ ].

1 is _____ fewer than 2.

8. 5 is how many fewer than 8?

[ ] minus [ ] is [ ].

5 is _____ fewer than 8.

TRY IT

9. 18 is how many more than 7?

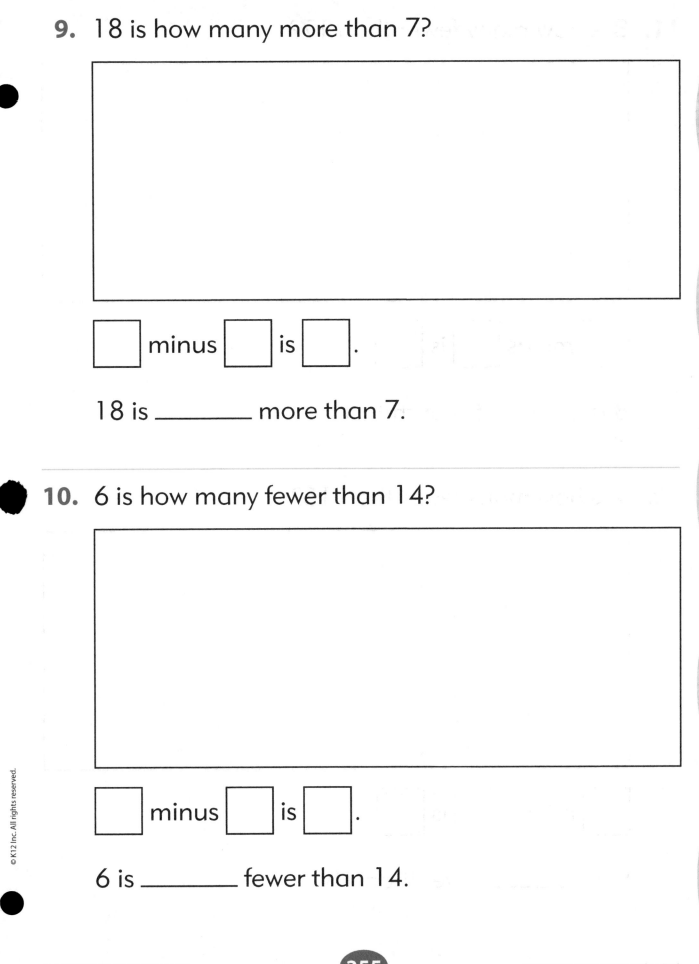

☐ minus ☐ is ☐.

18 is _____ more than 7.

---

10. 6 is how many fewer than 14?

☐ minus ☐ is ☐.

6 is _____ fewer than 14.

TRY IT

11. 8 is how many fewer than 17?

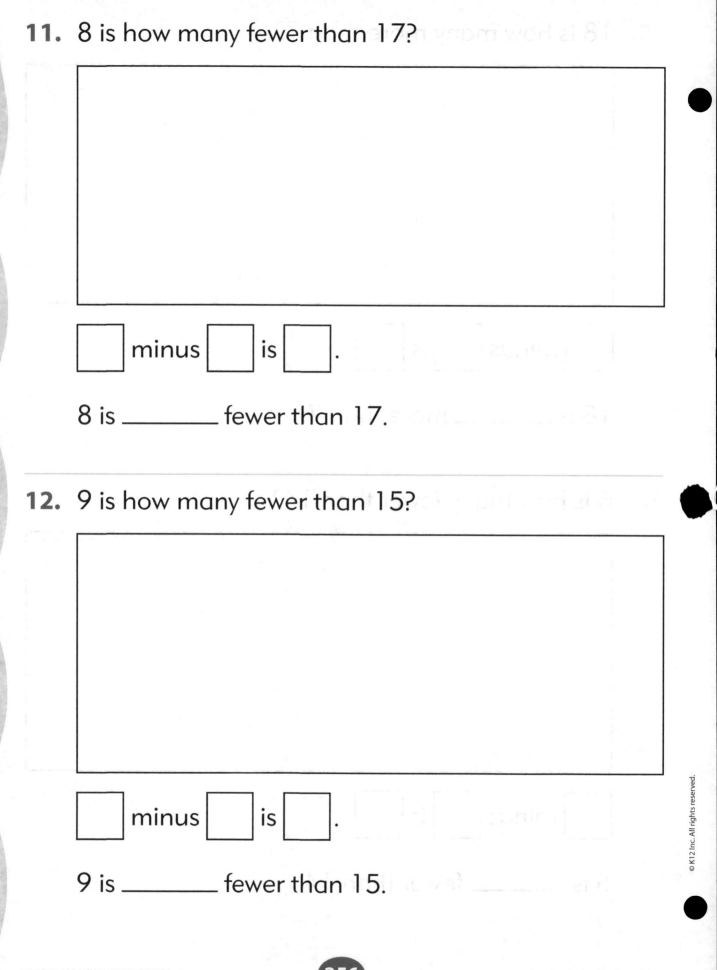

$\boxed{}$ minus $\boxed{}$ is $\boxed{}$.

8 is _____ fewer than 17.

12. 9 is how many fewer than 15?

$\boxed{}$ minus $\boxed{}$ is $\boxed{}$.

9 is _____ fewer than 15.

TRY IT

Take Away, Combine, and Compare
Solve Different Types of Problems

Use circle blocks or a sketch to solve.

1. Combine 5 and 13. What is the answer? _____

2. Take away 6 from 16. What is the answer? _____

3. 7 is how many fewer than 10? _____

4. What is 8 take away 2? _____

5. Add 4 and 9. What is the answer? _____

6. 18 is how many more than 14? _____

TRY IT

7. 11 is how many more than 6? _____

8. Combine 12 and 8. What is the answer? _____

9. What is 15 take away 14? _____

TRY IT

Compare to Subtract

Compare Numbers of Cubes

Use cubes to solve.

1. Show a group of 10 cubes
   Show a group of 3 cubes.

   How much greater is 10 than 3? _____

2. Show a group of 7 cubes.
   Show a group of 9 cubes.

   How much less is 7 than 9? _____

3. Make a cube train of 12 red cubes.
   Make a cube train of 8 red cubes.

   Compare. How much greater is 12 than 8? _____

4. Make a cube train of 8 red cubes.
   Make a cube train of 3 blue cubes.

   Compare. How much greater is 8 than 3? _____

5. Make a cube train of 15 red cubes.
   Make a cube train of 6 blue cubes.

   Compare. How much less is 6 than 15? _____

6. Make a cube train of 13 red cubes.
   Make a cube train of 5 blue cubes.

   Compare. How much less is 5 than 13? _____

TRY IT

Draw a picture or use cubes to solve.

7. How much less is 10 than 19?

8. How much less is 5 than 7?

9. How much more is 14 than 7?

10. How much more is 16 than 11?

TRY IT

Subtraction as Comparing

Draw Pictures to Compare

Complete the picture. Then answer the problem.

1. There are 8 children. There are 4 kites.

How many more children are there
than kites? _____

2. There are 6 swim masks. There are 3 snorkels.

How many fewer snorkels are there
than masks? _____

3. Look at the dots. How much greater is
16 than 8? _____

L E A R N

4. There are 15 sand pails.
There are 7 shovels.

How many more pails are there
than shovels?

_____

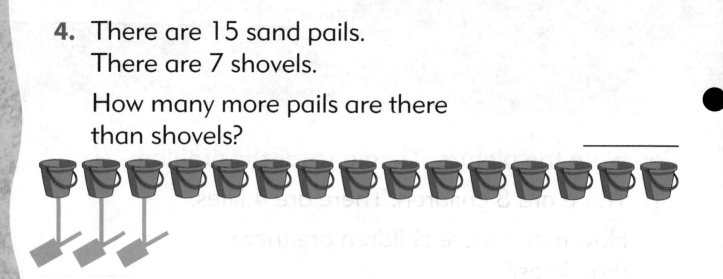

Draw a picture. Then answer the problem.

5. There are 12 green dots.
There are 7 black dots.

How many more green dots are
there than black dots?

_____

---

6. There are 19 red stars.
There are 2 blue stars.

How many more red stars are there than
blue stars?

_____

Subtraction as Comparing
Compare Numbers of Pictures

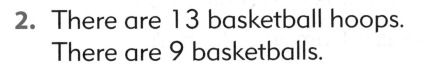

Name: _____

Complete the picture. Then answer the problem.

1. There are 12 baseballs. There are 9 bats.

   How many more baseballs are there than bats?

   _____

2. There are 13 basketball hoops.
   There are 9 basketballs.

   How many fewer basketballs are there than hoops?

   _____

Draw a picture. Then answer the problem.

3. There are 16 green circles.
   There are 8 yellow circles.

   How many more green circles are there
   than yellow circles?

   _____

T R Y   I T

4. There are 10 red circles.
There are 7 blue circles.

How many more red circles are there
than blue circles?

_____

5. There are 12 blue dots.
There are 4 green dots.

How many more blue dots are there
than green dots?

_____

6. There are 11 green dots and 5 blue dots.

How much more is 11 green dots than
5 blue dots?

_____

TRY IT

Comparison Subtraction
Solve Comparison Problems

Use a model or draw a picture to solve.

1. There are 17 cows.
   There are 9 horses.

   How many more cows are there
   than horses?   _____

2. There are 16 chickens near the barn.
   There are 10 sheep in a pen.

   How many fewer sheep are there
   than chickens?   _____

LEARN

3. Serena sees 19 ladybugs in the garden.
She also sees 13 bees.

How many more ladybugs than
bees are there? _____

4. There are 6 birds over the field.
There are 12 ducks in the pond.

How many more ducks than birds
are there? _____

5. There are 18 bales of hay.
There are 7 horses.

How many fewer horses are there
than bales of hay? _____

Comparison Subtraction
Compare and Subtract

Use a model or draw a picture to solve.

1. Rosa sees 15 sheep.
She also sees 9 goats.

How many more sheep than goats
are there?

_____

2. There are 17 chickens on the farm.
There are 8 pigs.

How many fewer pigs are there
than chickens?

_____

3. How much less is 3 than 15?

_____

4. How much more is 5 than 1?

_____

TRY IT

Circle the answer.

5. Barb has 9 flowers. John has 7 flowers.
How many more flowers does
Barb have than John?

Which of the following describes this situation?

A. Two numbers are added.

B. Two numbers are compared.

---

6. Caden has 4 trucks. Coleman has 11 trucks.
How many fewer trucks does Caden
have than Coleman?

Which of the following describes this situation?

A. Two numbers are added.

B. Two numbers are compared.

TRY IT

Unit Review

Checkpoint Practice

Name: _____

Draw a sketch to show how to solve.

1. 8 is how many more than 2?　　　　　_____

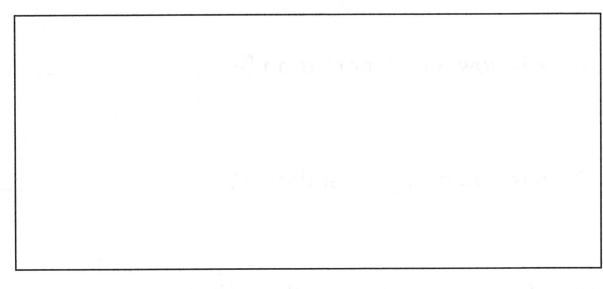

2. 7 is how many fewer than 15?　　　　_____

UNIT REVIEW

Use circle blocks to solve.

3. 10 is how many more than 5? _____

4. 7 is how many more than 6? _____

5. 6 is how many fewer than 9? _____

6. 7 is how many more than 2? _____

7. 4 is how many fewer than 10? _____

8. 7 is how many more than 5? _____

9. 4 is how many fewer than 15? _____

10. 19 is how many more than 6? _____

UNIT REVIEW

What's the Difference?
Compare Stories with Cubes and Sketches

Model the problem with cubes or sketches.
Write the answer.

1. Ethan has 7 fish.
He also has 2 crabs.

How many more fish than crabs does
Ethan have?

_____ more fish

---

2. Jack saw 2 blue boats.
He saw 4 red boats.

How many fewer blue boats than red boats
did Jack see?

_____ fewer blue boats

---

3. Emily picked 5 strawberries.
Ashley picked 8 strawberries.

How many fewer strawberries did Emily
pick than Ashley?

_____ fewer strawberries

L E A R N

4. Ricky has 3 toy trucks.
Al has 7 toy trucks.

How many more toy trucks does Al have than Ricky?

_____ more trucks

---

5. Michael has 8 crayons.
Beth has 2 crayons.

How many more crayons does Michael have than Beth?

_____ more crayons

---

6. Beth has 3 stuffed animals.
Taylor has 6 stuffed animals.

How many fewer stuffed animals does Beth have than Taylor?

_____ fewer stuffed animals

What's the Difference?

Solve Compare Problems

Model the problem with cubes or sketches.
Write the answer.

1. There are 8 children.
There are 7 fishing rods.

How many more children than fishing rods
are there?

_____ more child

2. Chad has 10 soccer balls.
He also has 4 footballs.

How many more soccer balls than footballs
does Chad have?

_____ more soccer balls

3. Hannah caught 8 butterflies.
Bridget caught 1 butterfly.

How many fewer butterflies did Bridget
catch than Hannah?

_____ fewer butterflies

4. There are 4 boys in the van.
There is 1 girl in the van.

How many more boys than girls are in the van?

_____ more boys

T R Y   I T

5. There are 3 ducks in the lake.
There are 9 ducks on the shore.

How many fewer ducks are in the lake than on the shore?

_____ fewer ducks in the lake

Place a check mark next to the picture you would use to solve the problem.

6. Valerie baked 8 cakes.
Helena baked 2 cakes.

How many more cakes did Valerie bake than Helena?

A.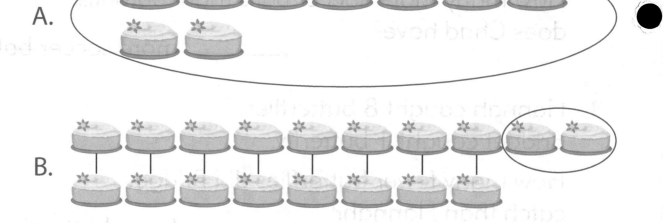

B.

C.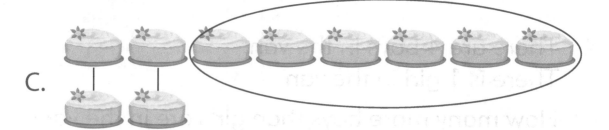

TRY IT

7. Ellie had 9 balloons.
Carrie had 7 balloons.

How many fewer balloons did Carrie have than Ellie?

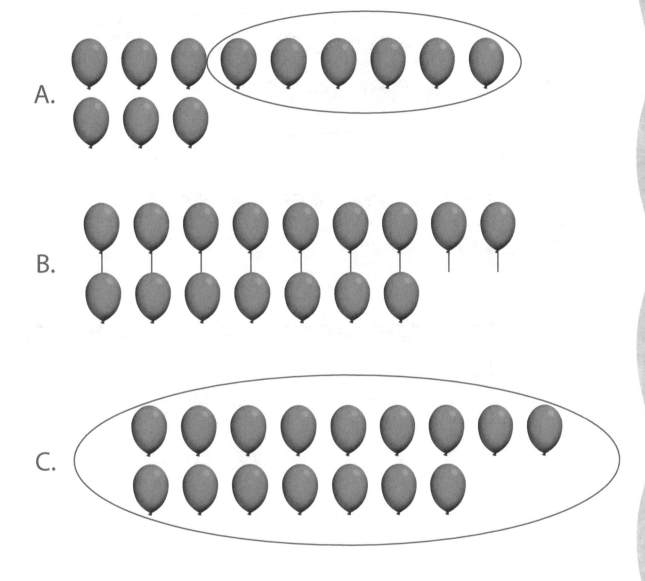

A.

B.

C.

TRY IT

8. Laura baked 6 pies.
Debbie baked 2 pies.

How many fewer pies did Debbie bake than Laura?

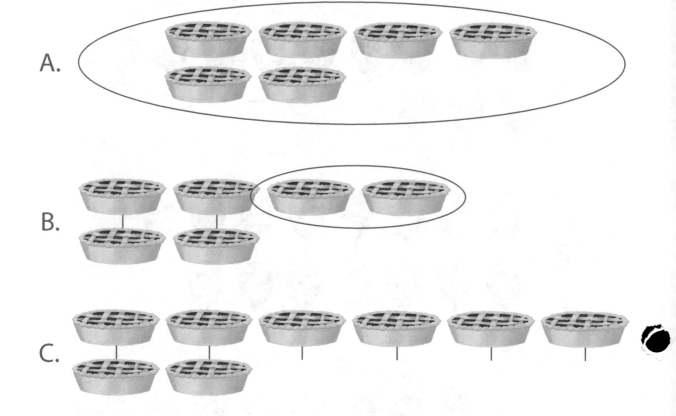

A.

B.

C.

TRY IT

Add and Subtract Story Problems

Solve Different Story Problems

Model the problem with cubes or sketches. Explain how you will solve the problem. Complete the number sentence and write the answer.

1. Jen has 1 flower in a pot.
   She has 8 flowers in a vase.

   How many flowers does Jen have in all?

   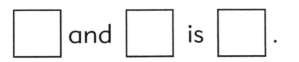

   _____ flowers in all

2. There were 6 carrots in a bucket.
   A horse ate 6 carrots.

   How many carrots are left in the bucket?

   _____ carrots left

T R Y I T

3. Bill has 9 green hats.
He also has 4 yellow hats.

How many more green hats than yellow hats
does Bill have?

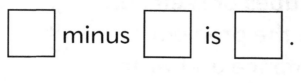

_____ more green hats

---

4. Jane has 5 stickers.
Vivian has 3 stickers.

How many stickers do they have in all?

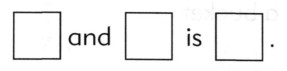

_____ stickers in all

TRY IT

Model the problem with cubes or sketches. Then complete the number sentence and write the answer.

5. Mark rode his bike 7 times this week. Kevin rode his bike 4 times this week.

   How many more times did Mark ride his bike than Kevin?

   [   ] minus [   ] is [   ] .

   _____ more times

6. Maria had 10 markers. She gave 2 markers to her sister.

   How many markers does Maria have left?

   [   ] take away [   ] is [   ] .

   _____ markers left

T R Y   I T

7. Mike ate 7 apple slices.
Gavin ate 1 apple slice.

How many fewer apples slices did Gavin
eat than Mike?

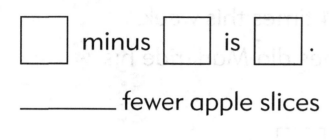

[ ] minus [ ] is [ ] .

_____ fewer apple slices

---

8. Robert has 2 red sailboats.
He also has 4 green sailboats.

How many sailboats does Robert have
in all?

[ ] and [ ] is [ ] .

_____ sailboats in all

TRY IT

Circle the answer.

1. Carly has 8 books. Liz has 5 books.

   Who has more books?

   A. Carly has more books.

   B. Liz has more books.

2. Jason has 4 apples. Nick has 1 apple.

   Who has fewer apples?

   A. Jason has fewer apples.

   B. Nick has fewer apples.

3. David has 8 rocks in his collection.
   Paul has 4 rocks in his collection.

   Who has more rocks?

   A. David has more rocks.

   B. Paul has more rocks.

4. Mara ran 4 miles. Brendan ran 1 mile.

   Who ran fewer miles?

   A. Mara ran fewer miles.

   B. Brendan ran fewer miles.

TRY IT

5. The chef made 8 pizzas. 1 bear came for a snack.

Are there more pizzas or bears?

   A. There are more pizzas.

   B. There are more bears.

Circle the answer. You may use cubes to help you.

6. David wants 3 scoops of ice cream.
Holly wants 2 scoops of ice cream.

How many fewer scoops of ice cream does Holly want than David?

   A. 5   B. 2   C. 1

---

7. There are 3 people in Jane's family.
Jane bought 5 ice cream sandwiches.

If each person eats 1 sandwich, how many will be left over?

   A. 1   B. 2   C. 3

Circle the answer.

8. Summer bought 8 roses. Merrie bought 10 roses.

How many fewer roses did Summer buy than Merrie?

   A. 9   B. 2   C. 6

9. Cameron read 5 pages. Eva read 10 pages.

How many more pages did Eva read then Cameron?

   A. 6   B. 5   C. 15

TRY IT

Compare: More or Fewer?

Find More and Fewer

Model the problem with circle blocks.
Write the answer.

1. The library has 6 animal magazines.
It has 4 sports magazines.

How many fewer sports magazines than animal magazines does the library have?

6 minus 4 is _____ .

_____ fewer sports magazines

---

2. A book about baseball has 9 pages.
A book about soccer has 10 pages.

How many more pages does the soccer book have than the baseball book?

10 minus 9 is _____ .

_____ more page

T R Y   I T

3. A shelf has 6 picture books.
It has 9 chapter books.

How many more chapter books than picture books are on the shelf?

9 minus 6 is _____ .

_____ more chapter books

---

4. On Monday, 7 children came to story hour.
On Tuesday, 2 children came to story hour.

How many fewer children came to story hour on Tuesday than on Monday?

7 minus 2 is _____ .

_____ fewer children

Choose how to solve the problem. Write the answer.

5. The first poem in the book has 10 lines.
The second poem has 8 lines.

How many fewer lines does the second poem have than the first poem?

10 minus 8 is _____ .

_____ fewer lines

TRY IT

6. Leon checked out 5 books on Tuesday. He checked out 2 books on Friday.

   How many more books did Leon check out on Tuesday than on Friday?

   5 minus 2 is _____ .

   _____ more books

Write the answer.

7. There are 3 books about desert animals. There are 8 books about sea animals.

   How many more books are about sea animals than books about desert animals?

   _____ more books

8. Kiki read 9 pages of her book in the morning. She read 2 pages in the afternoon.

   How many more pages did Kiki read in the morning than in the afternoon?

   _____ more pages

Compare in Everyday Situations

Write the answer.

1. Pat has 8 rocks in his collection.
   Chris has 4 rocks in her collection.

   How many rocks do they have together?

   _____ rocks altogether

2. Jack has 4 apples. Nancy has 1 apple.

   How many fewer apples does Nancy have than Jack?

   _____ fewer apples

3. Monty walked 4 blocks. Brenda walked 6 blocks.

   How many more blocks did Brenda walk?

   _____ more blocks

4. Paula put 6 crackers on her plate.
   Max ate 2 of Paula's crackers.

   How many crackers does Paula have to eat now?

   _____ crackers

TRY IT

5. The chef made 8 salads. He also made 5 pies.

How many more salads did he make than pies?

_____ more salads

6. Len has 10 books. Carl has 8 books.

How many fewer books does Carl have than Len?

_____ fewer books

Circle the answer.

7. Kevin bought 6 pens. Don bought 11 pens.

How many fewer pens did Kevin buy than Don?

A. 5   B. 6   C. 11

8. Patty read 4 pages. Eva read 10 pages.

How many more pages did Eva read than Patty?

A. 4   B. 6   C. 14

Make up a problem of your own that compares the numbers of animals. Solve your problem.

9. Pretend you have 2 dogs, 1 cat, and 3 hamsters. Make up a problem.

The answer to your problem:

_____

TRY IT

Estimate and Check Subtraction

Check Comparison Problems

Use circle blocks to check the answer to the problem. Circle Yes or No.

1. There are 17 strawberries.
   There are 7 blueberries.

   How many more strawberries are there than blueberries ?

   Serena says there are 10 more strawberries than blueberries.

   Is Serena's answer correct?

   A. Yes   B. No

2. There are 15 pickles in a jar.
   There are 4 pickles on a plate.

   How many fewer pickles are on the plate than in the jar?

   Alexander says there are 9 fewer pickles on the plate than in the jar.

   Is Alexander's answer correct?

   A. Yes   B. No

LEARN

Use sketches to check the answer to the problem. Circle Yes or No.

3. There are 20 pumpkins on a vine.
There are 8 pumpkins in a basket.

How many more pumpkins are on the vine than in the basket?

Serena says there are 14 more pumpkins on the vine than in the basket.

Is Serena's answer correct?

A. Yes   B. No

---

4. There are 13 cucumbers.
There is 1 carrot.

How many fewer carrots are there than cucumbers?

Alexander says there are 12 fewer carrots than cucumbers.

Is Alexander's answer correct?

A. Yes   B. No

Estimate and Check Subtraction

Estimate and Check Comparisons

Determine the benchmark for each number in the problem. Then circle the best estimate for the answer.

1. About how many more is 18 pears than 9 pears?

   A. about 5   B. about 10

   C. about 15   D. about 20

2. About how many more is 13 pineapples than 9 pineapples?

   A. about 5   B. about 10

   C. about 15   D. about 20

3. There are 16 cherries in a bowl, and 4 cherries on a table. About how many more cherries are in the bowl than on the table?

   A. about 5   B. about 10

   C. about 15   D. about 20

4. There are 3 birds in the tree and 9 birds on the fence. About how many fewer birds are in the tree than on the fence?

   A. about 5   B. about 10

   C. about 15   D. about 20

TRY IT

Use cubes or sketches to check the answer.
Then circle Yes or No.

5. There are 10 apples in a basket.
There are 3 apples on a table.

How many fewer apples are on the table than in the basket?

Alexander says there are 5 fewer apples on the table than in the basket.

Is Alexander's answer correct?

A. Yes   B. No

6. There are 16 shells in a bowl, and 6 shells in a pail. There are 11 more shells in the bowl than in the pail.

Is this answer correct?

A. Yes   B. No

7. At the park, 12 girls rode on the swings and 5 girls went down the slide. So 7 more girls rode the swings than went down the slide.

Is this answer correct?

A. Yes   B. No

8. Wilma has 6 marbles. Jake has 8 marbles.
Wilma has 2 fewer marbles than Jake.

Is this answer correct?

A. Yes   B. No

TRY IT

Unit Review

Checkpoint Practice

Write the answer. You may use models or sketches to help you.

1. Tara did 6 word puzzles.
   She also did 3 number puzzles.

   Did Tara do more word puzzles or number puzzles?

   Circle the answer.

   A. word puzzles   B. number puzzles

   How many more? _____ more

---

2. Cole has 4 sand buckets.
   Chad has 3 sand buckets.

   How many sand buckets do they have in all?

   _____ sand buckets

---

3. There were 8 lions resting in the sun, and then 5 of the lions moved under a tree.

   How many lions are still resting in the sun?

   _____ lions

4. Michael's Pet Store has 7 white kittens and 2 brown kittens.

How many fewer brown kittens are there than white kittens?

_____ fewer brown kittens

Circle the answer.

5. There are 4 fruit bars.
There are 2 children.

Are there more fruit bars or children?

A. fruit bars   B. children

6. If you take away 4 marbles from 12 marbles, do you have 6 marbles left?

A. Yes   B. No

7. Pat made 10 sandwiches and Lisa made 8 sandwiches. How many more sandwiches did Pat make than Lisa?

A. 8   B. 6   C. 2

UNIT REVIEW

8. Jack has 9 books.
He has already read 3 of the books.

About how many books does Jack have left
to read?

A. about 5   B. about 10   C. about 15

9. There are 15 mice.
There are 3 cubes of cheese.

How many fewer cubes of cheese are there
than mice?

Ben says there are 12 fewer cubes of cheese
than mice.

Is Ben's answer correct?

A. Yes   B. No

10. Alice had 11 toys.
She gave 5 toys to her little sister.

About how many toys does Alice have left?

A. about 5   B. about 10   C. about 15

Use circle blocks to explain how to solve the problem.

11. Olivia bought 4 new shirts.
    Paige bought 3 new shirts.

    How many more shirts did Olivia buy than Paige?

Use cubes to explain how to solve the problem.

12. Sylvie bought 4 new T-shirts, and Alice bought 1 T-shirt.

    How many T-shirts did they buy altogether?

Different Types of Problems

A Variety of Problems

Explain how to solve the problem. Then circle Add or Subtract.

1. Molly had 8 crayons.
She gave 2 crayons to her brother.

How many crayons does Molly have left?

A. Add   B. Subtract

2. 7 bees were on a flower.
3 more bees flew up and landed on the flower.

How many bees are on the flower now?

A. Add   B. Subtract

3. Peter made 10 greeting cards.
He gave 4 of them to his friends.

How many greeting cards does Peter have left?

A. Add   B. Subtract

4. Emily ate 4 plums.
Colin ate 12 plums.

How many plums did they eat altogether?

A. Add   B. Subtract

TRY IT

5. 6 squirrels ran up the tree.
Then 2 more squirrels ran up the tree.

How many squirrels are in the tree altogether?

A. Add   B. Subtract

---

6. Jillian has 6 dolls.
Perry has 4 dolls.

How many more dolls does Jillian have than Perry?

A. Add   B. Subtract

---

7. Edward has 7 cats.
George has 4 cats.

How many fewer cats does George have than Edward?

A. Add   B. Subtract

---

8. Jody collected 7 stones.
Susie collected 13 stones.

How many stones did they collect altogether?

A. Add   B. Subtract

TRY IT

Combine and Change Problems

More Problems

Write the answer.

1. Mark made 7 pizzas.
   He then made 3 more pizzas.

   How many pizzas did Mark make altogether?

   Mark made _____ pizzas altogether.

2. Jack was given 10 marbles.
   He already had 7 marbles.

   How many marbles does Jack have now?

   Jack has _____ marbles now.

Circle the answer.

3. Which expression should be used to solve this problem?

   A rabbit had 10 carrots.
   It ate 3 of them.

   How many carrots are left?

   A. $3 + 10$ B. $10 + 3$ C. $10 - 3$

TRY IT

Write the answer.

4. Shannon has 5 blue stones.
   Dylan has 5 red stones.

   How many stones do they have altogether?

   They have _____ stones altogether.

5. Billy has 13 pears.
   Tommy has 3 pears.

   How many pears do they have altogether?

   They have _____ pears altogether.

6. Hank has 12 baseball cards.
   Donnie has 8 baseball cards.

   How many baseball cards do they have altogether?

   They have _____ baseball cards altogether.

7. Lucas has 3 teddy bears.
   Kevin has 5 teddy bears.

   How many teddy bears do they have altogether?

   They have _____ teddy bears altogether.

TRY IT

Circle the answer.

8. Which should be done to solve this problem?

   Ella made 12 quilts.
   She gave 5 to her friends.

   How many quilts does Ella have now?

   A. Compare 12 and 5 to see which is larger.

   B. Put 12 and 5 together.

   C. Take 5 away from 12.

9. Which expression should be used to solve this problem?

   10 rabbits were in the garden.
   4 of them ran away.

   How many rabbits are left in the garden?

   A. $10 + 4$ B. $10 - 4$ C. $4 - 10$

10. Which expression should be used to solve this problem?

    Peter had 17 stamps in his collection.
    He got 3 more stamps from his brother.

    How many stamps does Peter have now?

    A. $17 - 3$ B. $17 + 3$ C. $3 - 17$

T R Y   I T

Compare and Combine Problems

Farm Combinations

Color the pictures to solve.

1. Sunshine Farm has 11 roosters.
   It has 9 brown roosters.
   The rest of the roosters are black.

   How many roosters are black?

   11 minus 9 is _____. $\boxed{11} \bigcirc{-} \boxed{9} \bigcirc{=} \boxed{}$

   Sunshine Farm has _____ black roosters.

2. The farmer planted 8 rows of tomato plants.
   3 rows now have red tomatoes.
   The rest of the rows have orange tomatoes.

   How many rows have orange tomatoes?

   8 minus 3 is _____. $\boxed{8} \bigcirc{-} \boxed{} \bigcirc{=} \boxed{}$

   There are _____ rows of orange tomatoes.

LEARN

3. Mrs. Wan uses 12 apples from the farm to make pies.
She has 6 green apples.
The rest of her apples are red.

How many red apples are there?

12 minus 6 is _____.   12 ◯ ▢ ⊜ ▢

Mrs. Wan has _____ red apples.

---

4. 10 cows are grazing in the field.
2 cows have brown spots.
The rest have black spots.

How many cows have black spots?

10 minus 2 is _____.   ▢ ◯ ▢ ◯ ▢

There are _____ cows with black spots.

Name:

Compare and Combine Problems

Compare and Combine

Write the answer.

1. Yubo wrote 9 stories. Cate wrote 3 fewer stories than Yubo.

   How many stories did Cate write?

   Cate wrote _____ stories.

2. Yuki practices judo 5 times per week. Sam practices judo 2 fewer times than Yuki.

   How many times does Sam practice judo a week?

   Sam practices judo _____ times a week.

3. Steven has 12 cats. 5 cats are brown and the rest are white.

   How many white cats does Steven have?

   Steven has _____ white cats.

4. Carrie ate 10 strawberries. Haley ate 1 strawberry.

   How many more strawberries did Carrie eat than Haley?

   Carrie ate _____ more strawberries than Haley.

TRY IT

ADD OR SUBTRACT: PROBLEM SOLVING

305

COMPARE AND COMBINE PROBLEMS

Circle the answer.

5. Manuela has 14 stuffed animals.
10 of them are dogs and the rest are bears.

How many stuffed bears does Manuela have?

    A. 4   B. 5   C. 6

6. Katy has 15 dog treats.
12 of the dog treats are round and the rest are square.

How many dog treats are square?

    A. 3   B. 4   C. 5

7. Stephanie has 10 crayons.
6 crayons are yellow and the rest are black.

How many black crayons does Stephanie have?

    A. 4   B. 6   C. 16

8. Carol made 3 sandwiches.
Margo made 8 sandwiches.

Who made fewer sandwiches?

    A. Carol   B. Margo

TRY IT

Change and Compare Problems

Solving Problems

Write the answer.

1. Look at the two problems. Solve the problem that asks about changing the number of stamps that Harold has.

   Problem 1

   Harold has 6 stamps. Brent has 3 stamps.

   How many fewer stamps does Brent have than Harold?

   Problem 2

   Harold had 6 stamps.
   Brent gave him 3 more stamps.

   How many stamps does Harold have now?

   Which problem did you solve?

   A. Problem 1   B. Problem 2

   Answer: _____ stamps

2. Frida had 7 books. James gave her some more books. Frida now has 10 books. How many books did James give Frida?

   James gave Frida _____ more books.

TRY IT

Circle the answer.

3. Mason has 4 baseballs.
Ciera has 10 baseballs.

How many fewer baseballs does Mason
have than Ciera?

A. 4   B. 10   C. 6

---

4. Which choice best describes what is
happening in this problem?

> Tanya had 9 crayons.
> She gave 3 crayons to Jackie. How many crayons
> does Tanya have left?

A. Tanya now has more than 9 crayons.

B. Tanya now has 9 crayons.

C. Tanya now has fewer than 9 crayons.

---

5. Which problem asks about comparing the
number of apples?

A. Sharla has 6 apples. Jenny has 4 apples.
How many fewer apples does Jenny have than
Sharla?

B. Sharla has 6 apples. Jenny has 4 apples.
How many apples do they have altogether?

TRY IT

6. Which problem talks about something being taken away?

    A. Sam had 10 baseball cards.
       He gave 4 to his brother.
       How many cards does Sam have now?

    B. Anna has 7 candies.
       Maria has 6 candies.
       How many candies do they have altogether?

    C. There are 3 rabbits and 6 carrots.
       If each rabbit gets 1 carrot, how many
       carrots will be left over?

Write the answer.

7. Sophie had 6 pears.
    She gave 2 pears to Molly.

    How many pears does Sophie have left?

    Sophie has _____ pears left.

---

8. Conner has 5 baseball hats and 3 visors.

    How many more baseball hats does Conner
    have than visors?

    Conner has _____ more baseball hats
    than visors.

TRY IT

9. Look at the two problems. Solve the problem that asks you to compare the number of sailboats.

Problem 1

George saw 7 sailboats.
Amanda saw 3 sailboats.

How many sailboats did they see altogether?

Problem 2

George saw 7 sailboats.
Amanda saw 3 sailboats.

How many more sailboats did George see than Amanda?

Which problem did you solve?

A. Problem 1   B. Problem 2

Answer: _____ sailboats

---

10. Grant had painted 3 toy cars.
He painted another 4 toy cars.

How many toy cars did Grant paint altogether?

Grant painted _____ toy cars altogether.

Write the answer. You may use cubes or sketches.

1. Kate had 8 necklaces.
    She was given 5 more necklaces.

    How many necklaces does Kate have now?

    Kate has _____ necklaces now.

2. Mrs. Nelson bought 11 bagels.
    Her family ate 5 bagels for breakfast.

    How many bagels are left?

    There are _____ bagles left.

3. Adam made 7 baskets.
    Nick made 4 baskets.

    How many baskets did they make altogether?

    They made _____ baskets altogether.

4. There are 12 juice boxes.
There are 7 apple juice boxes and the rest are grape.

How many juice boxes are grape?

There are _____ grape juice boxes.

5. There are 10 girls in the park.
There are 9 boys in the park.

How many fewer boys are there than girls?

There is _____ fewer boy.

6. There are 8 basketballs.
There are 4 soccer balls.

How many more basketballs are there than soccer balls?

There are _____ more basketballs than soccer balls.

7. Seth found 10 seashells at the beach.
Rachel also found 10 seashells.

How many seashells did they find altogether?

They found _____ seashells altogether.

8. Jim has 10 flowers.

4 flowers are red and the rest are yellow.

How many yellow flowers does Jim have?

Jim has _____ yellow flowers.

---

9. Colleen and Paula went to the circus.
Colleen counted 9 clowns.
Paula counted 7 clowns.

How many fewer clowns did Paula count than Colleen?

Paula counted _____ fewer clowns than Colleen.

Circle the answer.

10. Which shows a way to solve this problem?

Barry bought 6 bottles of water.
He drank 3 of them.

How many bottles of water does Barry have left?

A. $6 - 3$ B. $3 - 6$ C. $6 + 3$

11. Which problem talks about something being taken away?

A. Gina had 8 cookies and Manny had 3 cookies. How many cookies did they have altogether?

B. Sally had 14 balloons. Then 3 of the balloons popped. How many balloons does Sally have now?

C. Jimmy scored 8 goals and Harry scored 11 goals. How many more goals did Harry score than Jimmy?

---

12. Which problem asks about comparing the number of fish?

A. Serena had 7 fish. She gave 3 fish to Gavin. How many fish does Serena have now?

B. Serena has 7 fish. Gavin has 3 fish. How many more fish does Serena have than Gavin?

C. Serena has 7 fish. Gavin has 3 fish. How many fish do they have altogether?

Measure Objects

Measure Length

Measure the object. Write the answer.

1. Use cubes to measure the book.
   How long is the book?   _____ cubes

2. Use cubes to measure the shoe.
   How long is the shoe?   _____ cubes

3. How long is the marker?

   _____ paper clips

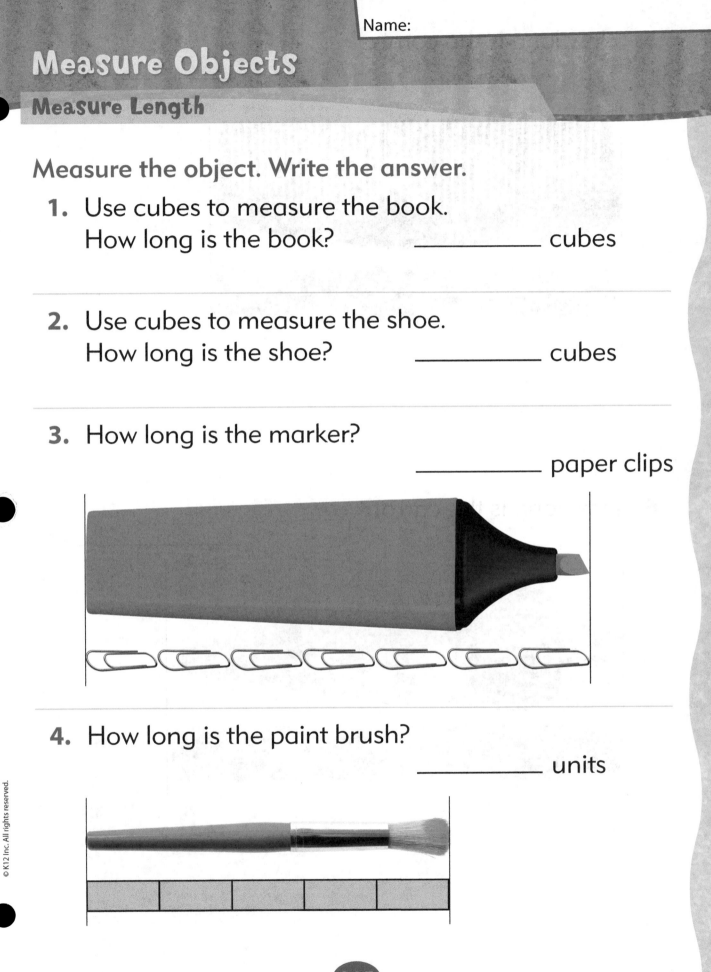

4. How long is the paint brush?

   _____ units

TRY IT

5. How long is the comb?

_____ beads

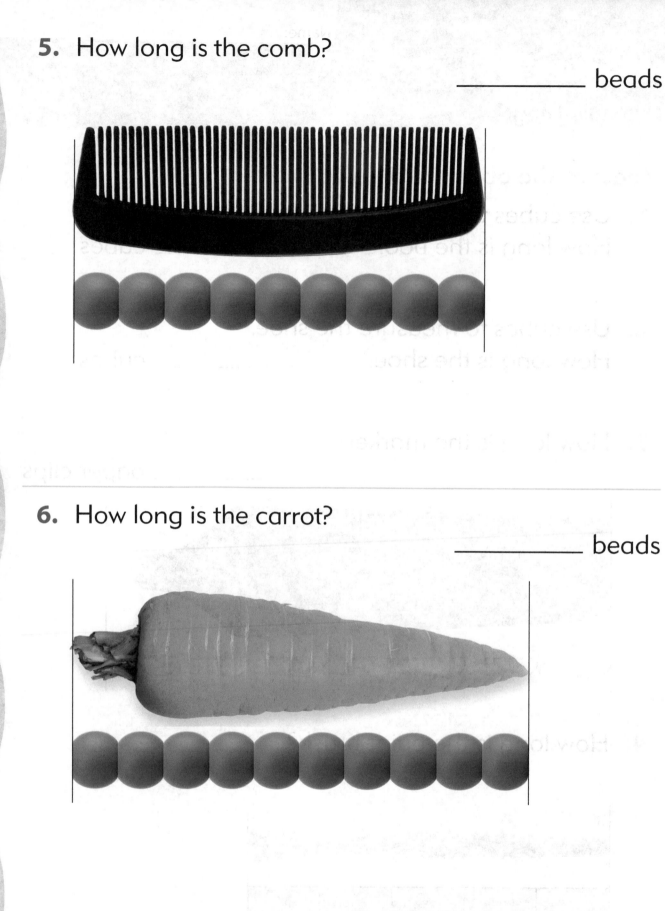

6. How long is the carrot?

_____ beads

TRY IT

Compare Length

Compare Length of Objects

Compare the objects. Circle the answer.

1. Which one is longer?

   A.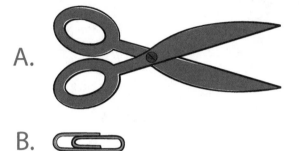

   B.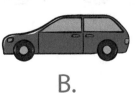

2. Which one is shorter?

   A.   B.

3. Which one is taller?

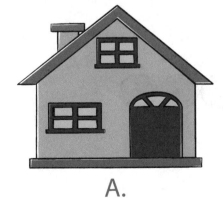

   A.   B.

T R Y   I T

4. Which one is shorter?

A.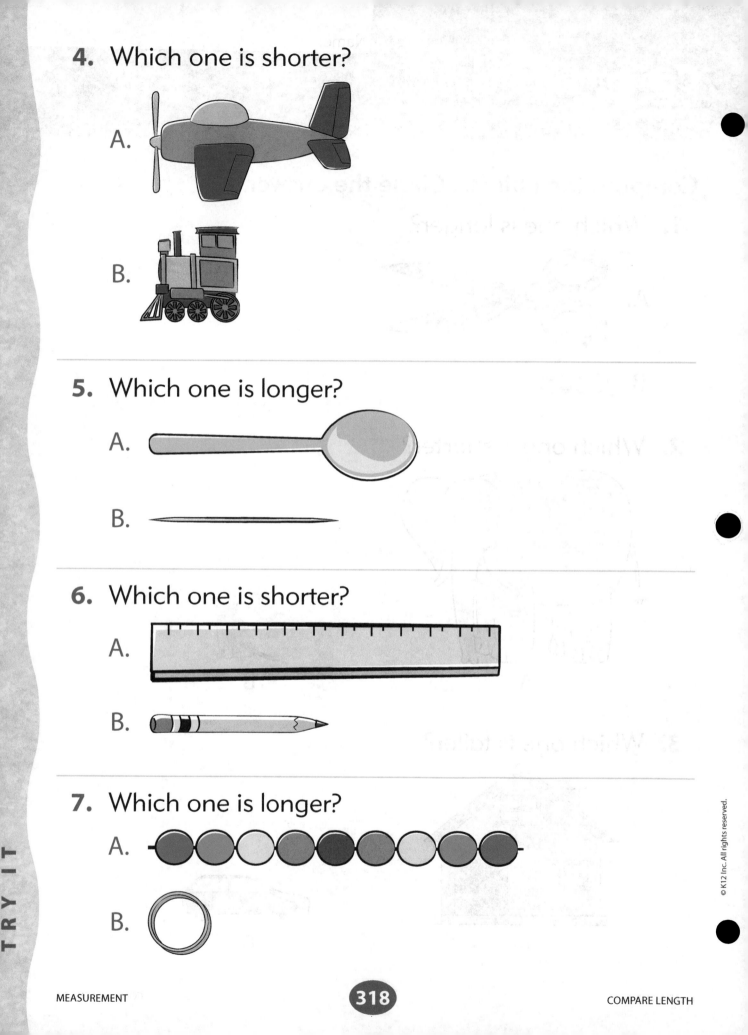

B.

5. Which one is longer?

A.

B.

6. Which one is shorter?

A.

B.

7. Which one is longer?

A.

B.

TRY IT

Compare Weight
Weight Comparison

Pick two objects and compare their weight.

1. Hold a _____ and a _____.
Draw a picture of the object that is heavier.

2. Hold a _____ and a _____.
Draw a picture of the object that is lighter.

Circle the answer.

3. Which object is lighter?

T R Y   I T

4. Which object is heavier?

---

5. Pick up the book in one hand and a sheet of paper in the other. Which is lighter?

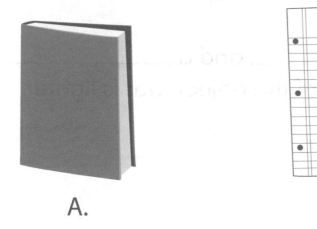

A.   B.

---

6. Pick up the book in one hand and a pencil in the other. Which is heavier?

A.   B.

TRY IT

Name:

Compare Capacity

Pick two objects and compare their capacity.

1. Fill a _____ and _____.
   Draw a picture of the container that holds more.

2. Fill a _____ and _____.
   Draw a picture of the container that holds more.

3. Fill a _____ and _____.
   Draw a picture of the container that holds less.

4. Fill a _____ and _____.
   Draw a picture of the container that holds less.

TRY IT

Compare the containers. Circle the answer.

5. Winnie used a cup to measure how much water each container holds. She wrote how many cups of water each holds under the containers.

Which container holds more?

2 cups

8 cups

---

6. Rosa used a cup to measure how much sand each container holds. She wrote how many cups of sand each holds under the containers.

Which container holds less?

3 cups

5 cups

TRY IT

Name:

Unit Review

Checkpoint Practice

Measure the object. Write the answer.

1. How long is the train?

_____ paper clips

Compare the objects. Circle the answer.

2. Which object is shorter?

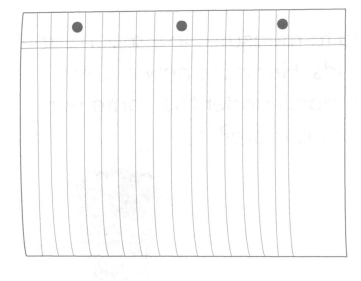

3. Which object is shorter?

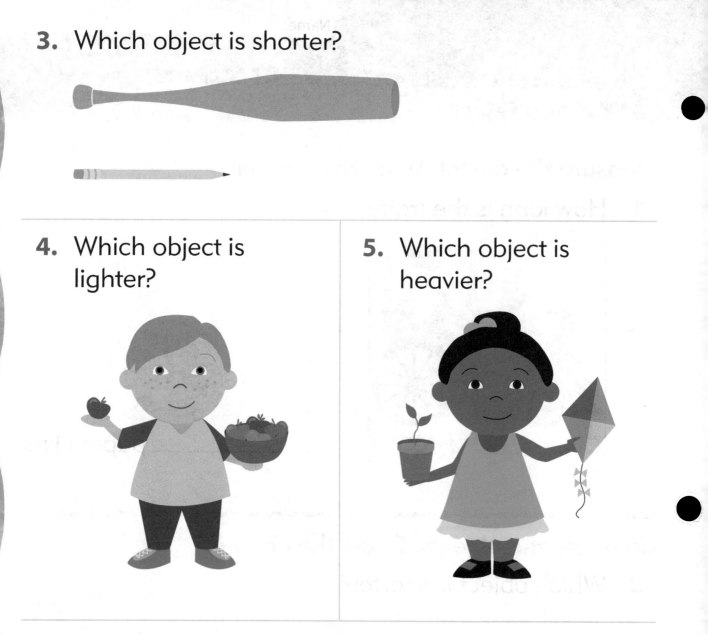

4. Which object is lighter?

5. Which object is heavier?

6. Johnny used a cup to measure how much sand each container holds. He wrote how many cups of sand each holds under the containers. Which container holds more?

2 cups

8 cups

Count and Show Numbers Through 30

Count and Show Numbers

Count the fruit. Cross out each piece of fruit as you count. Circle the answer.

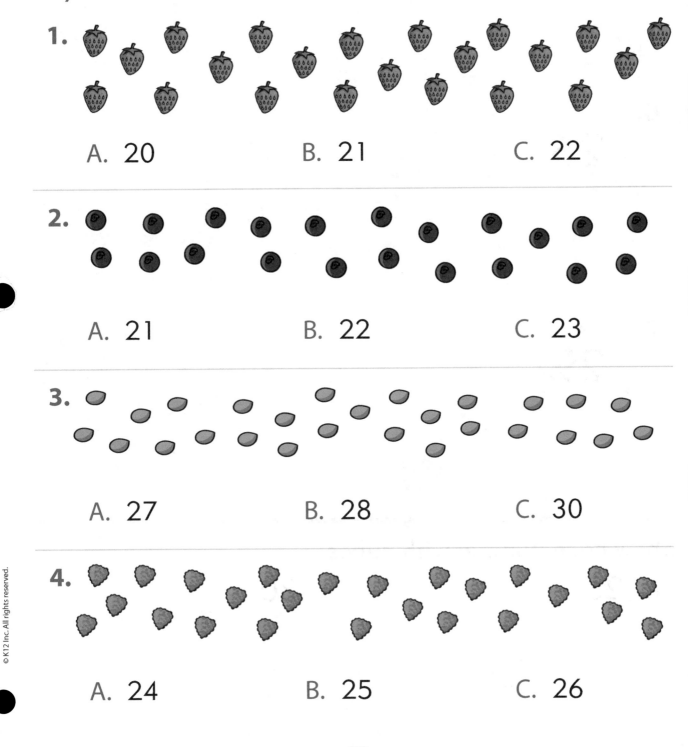

1.

   A. 20   B. 21   C. 22

2.

   A. 21   B. 22   C. 23

3.

   A. 27   B. 28   C. 30

4.

   A. 24   B. 25   C. 26

T R Y   I T

Draw dots or lines to show the number on the tile. Count aloud as you draw.

5.
23

6.
26

7.
29

Show each number with cubes.

8. 23

9. 30

TRY IT

Count Objects Through 30

Count Gems

Count aloud the number of gems shown.
Mark each one as you count.

1.

2.

3.

TRY IT

Count the gems.
Circle the number.

4.

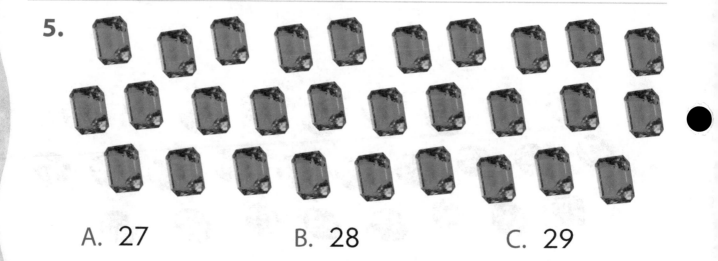

A. 22   B. 23   C. 24

5.

A. 27   B. 28   C. 29

6.

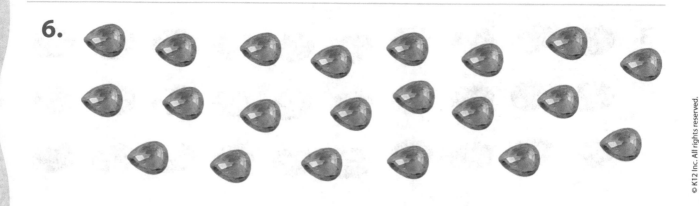

A. 21   B. 22   C. 23

TRY IT

Name:

Represent Amounts Through 30

Show and Draw Amounts

Draw dots or lines to show each number.
Draw rows of 10. Count aloud as you draw.

1. 27

2. 15

3. 22

4. 30

TRY IT

5. 25

6. 26

Show each number with cubes.
Show rows of 10.

7. 26

8. 23

9. 29

10. 24

TRY IT

Compare Groups Through 30

Compare Plant Groups

Read each problem and follow the directions.

1. Circle the group that has more flowers. Then draw an X on the group that has fewer flowers.

2. Alexander is growing 2 patches of flowers. One patch has 29 flowers. The other patch has 22 flowers. Circle the group with more flowers.

3. The red packet has 30 seeds and the green packet has 19 seeds. Circle the group with fewer seeds.

LEARN

4. Circle the groups that have an equal number of seeds in them.

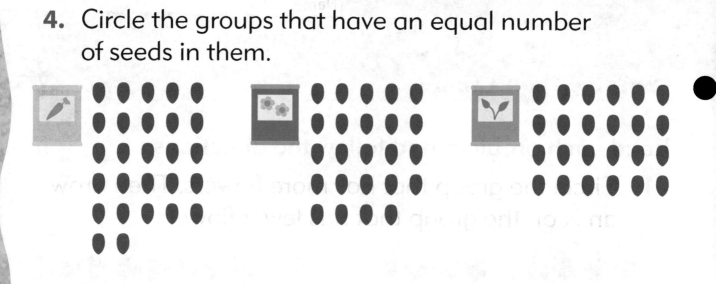

5. Circle the group with the most flowers. Then draw an X on the group with the fewest flowers.

❀❀❀❀❀❀❀❀❀❀
❀❀❀❀❀❀❀❀❀❀
❀   ✿✿✿✿✿✿✿✿✿✿   ✹✹✹✹✹✹✹✹✹✹
             ✿✿✿✿✿✿✿✿✿✿   ✹✹✹✹✹✹✹✹✹✹
             ✿✿✿✿✿✿   ✹✹✹✹✹

6. Circle the group with the most peppers. Then draw an X on the group with the fewest peppers.

LEARN

Compare Groups Through 30

Compare Groups

Read the problem and follow the directions.

1. Circle the group that has fewer flowers.

2. Circle the two groups that have an equal number of pebbles in them.

T R Y   I T

3. Circle the group with the most leaves.
Draw an X on the group with the fewest leaves.

4. Alexander picked 12 flowers. His grandmother picked 21 flowers. Who picked more flowers? Circle that picture.

Alexander   Grandmother

TRY IT

Groups in a Picture Graph

Show More or Fewer

Cut out each train car.

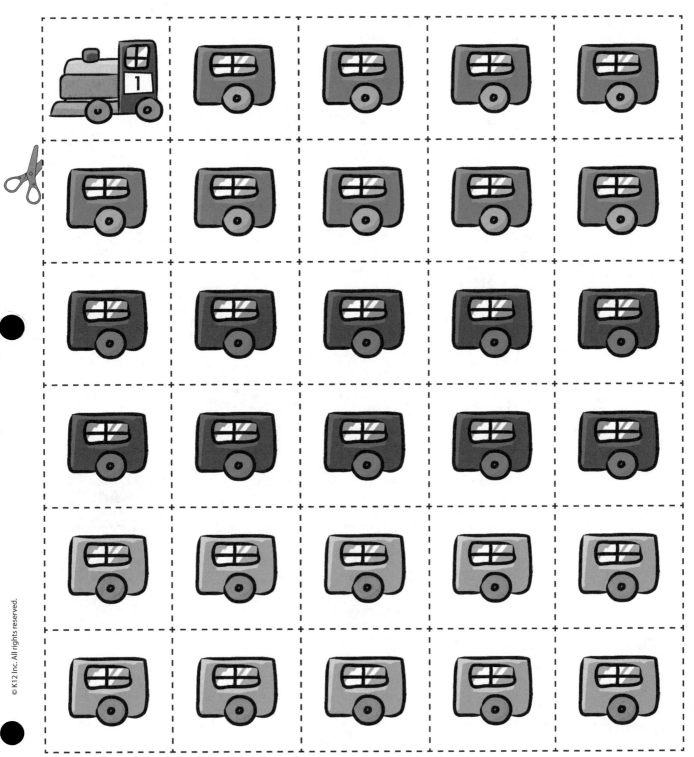

L E A R N

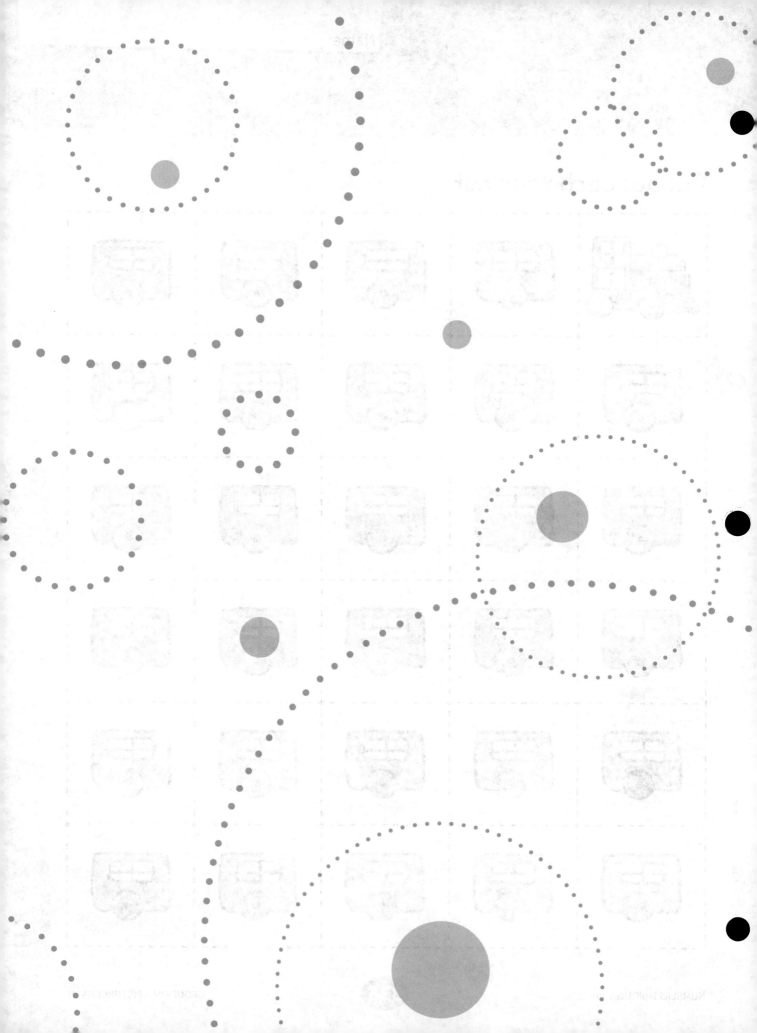

Groups in a Picture Graph

Compare Sets

Use the picture graph for Problems 1–3.
Circle the answer.

Tyler's Toys

🚗	🚗	🚗	🚗	🚗	🚗	🚗	🚗	🚗	🚗	🚗	🚗	🚗	🚗	🚗
🚚	🚚	🚚	🚚	🚚	🚚	🚚	🚚	🚚	🚚					
✈️	✈️	✈️	✈️	✈️	✈️	✈️	✈️							
🚂	🚂	🚂	🚂	🚂	🚂	🚂	🚂	🚂	🚂					

Each picture in the boxes equals 1.

1. Which **two** rows in the picture graph have the same number of toys?

A.    B.   C.   D.

2. Which row in the picture graph has the most toys?

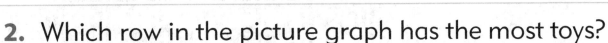

A.   B.   C.   D.

3. Which row in the picture graph has the fewest toys?

A.   B.   C.   D.

T R Y   I T

Circle the answer.

4. Which group has the fewest tires?

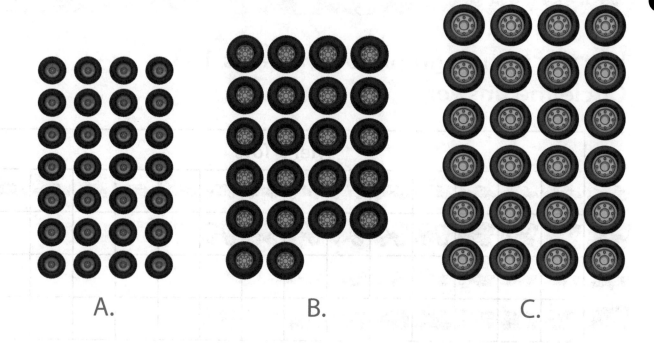

A.   B.   C.

5. Jordan collected 21 bus stamps. Taylor collected 25 bus stamps. Who collected more stamps?

A. Jordan

B. Taylor

TRY IT

6. Which group has more footballs?

A.

B.

7. Which group has fewer soccer balls?

A.

B.

8. Which group has the most tennis balls?

A.

B.

C.

T R Y   I T

9. Which group has the fewest cubes?

A.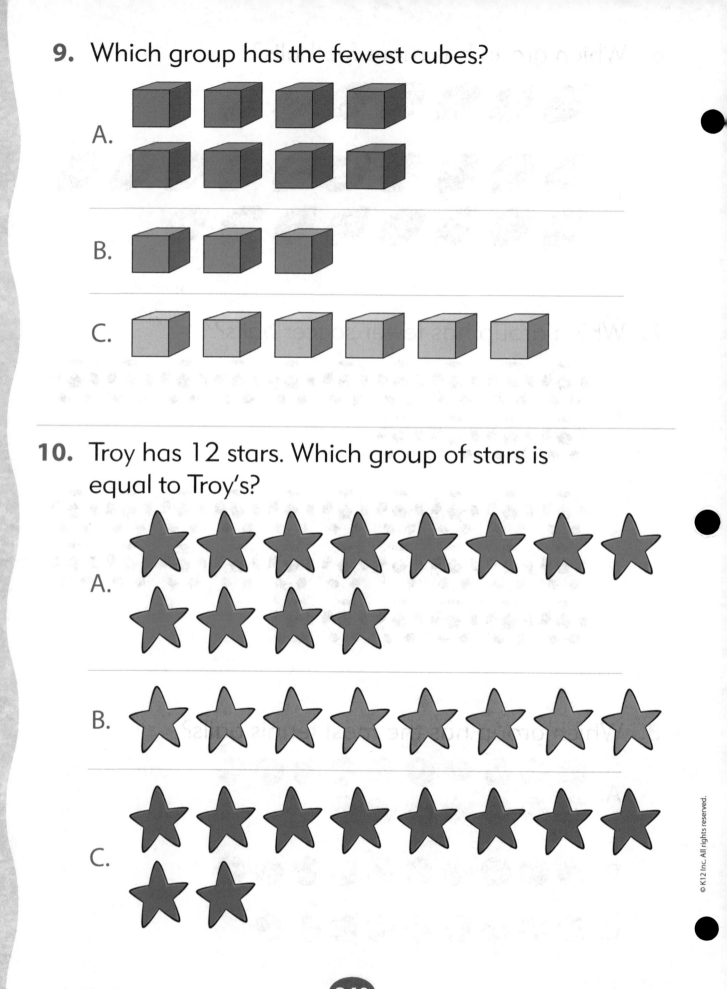

B.

C.

10. Troy has 12 stars. Which group of stars is equal to Troy's?

A.

B.

C.

TRY IT

Write Numerals Through 30

Write 1 Through 30

Name:

Write the number of insects shown in the problem.

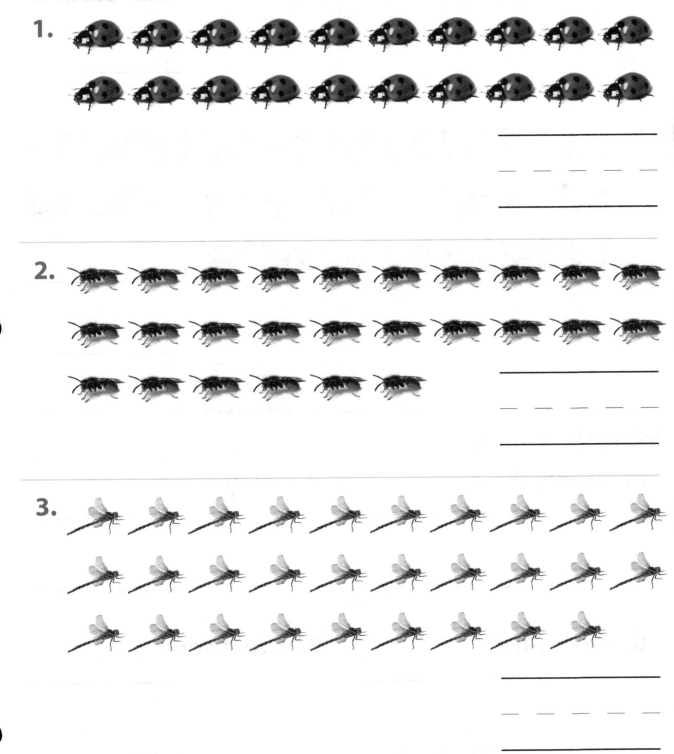

1.

2.

3.

_____

\- \- \- \- \- \-

_____

T R Y   I T

4.

_____

– – – – – – – – – – –

_____

5.

_____

– – – – – – – – – – –

_____

Write the number.

6. twenty-three

_____

– – – – – – –

_____

7. thirty

_____

– – – – – – –

_____

8. twenty-five

_____

– – – – – – –

_____

9. twenty-one

_____

– – – – – – –

_____

TRY IT

Name:

Count aloud the pictures in each row of the picture graph. Use the data for Problems 1–4. Circle the answer.

Jack's Aquarium													
🐢	🐢	🐢	🐢	🐢	🐢	🐢	🐢	🐢					
🐟	🐟	🐟	🐟	🐟	🐟	🐟	🐟	🐟	🐟	🐟	🐟	🐟	🐟
🐠	🐠	🐠	🐠	🐠	🐠	🐠	🐠	🐠	🐠	🐠			
🐌	🐌	🐌	🐌	🐌	🐌	🐌							

Each picture in the boxes equals 1.

1. Which row on the picture graph has the most objects?

   A. 🐢   B. 🐟   C. 🐠   D. 🐌

2. Does Jack have a greater number of goldfish or snails?

   A. 🐠   B. 🐌

3. Does Jack have fewer snails or turtles?

   A. 🐌   B. 🐢

4. Does Jack have more goldfish or turtles?

   A. 🐠   B. 🐢

LEARN

Count aloud the pictures in each row of the picture graph. Use data for Problems 5–8. Circle the answer.

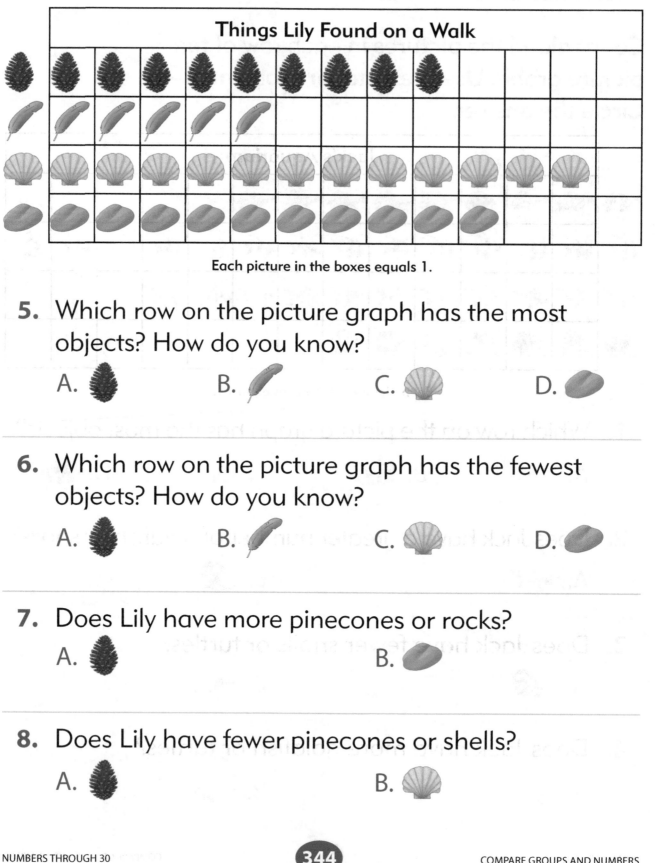

Things Lily Found on a Walk

Each picture in the boxes equals 1.

5. Which row on the picture graph has the most objects? How do you know?

   A. ![pinecone]   B. ![feather]   C. ![shell]   D. ![rock]

6. Which row on the picture graph has the fewest objects? How do you know?

   A. ![pinecone]   B. ![feather]   C. ![shell]   D. ![rock]

7. Does Lily have more pinecones or rocks?

   A. ![pinecone]   B. ![rock]

8. Does Lily have fewer pinecones or shells?

   A. ![pinecone]   B. ![shell]

Compare Groups and Numbers

Greater and Lesser Numbers

Use the data on the picture graph for Problems 1–3.
Circle the answer.

Types of Trees at the Park											
Maple	🍁	🍁	🍁	🍁	🍁	🍁	🍁	🍁			
Oak	🍂	🍂	🍂	🍂	🍂	🍂	🍂	🍂	🍂	🍂	🍂
Elm	🍃	🍃	🍃	🍃	🍃	🍃	🍃	🍃	🍃	🍃	
Birch	🍃	🍃	🍃	🍃	🍃	🍃	🍃	🍃	🍃		

Each picture in the boxes equals 1.

1. Are there more maple trees or oak trees at the park?

   A.   B.

2. Are there fewer maple trees or elm trees?

   A.   B.

3. Does the park have a greater number of oak trees
   or birch trees?

   A.   B.

TRY IT

Read the problem and circle the answer.

4. One group has 29 and the other group has 24. Which is the lesser number?

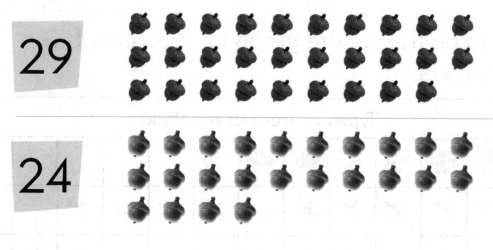

| 29 | |
| 24 | |

5. Which is more, 26 twigs or 21 twigs?

| 26 | |
| 21 | |

6. Which is fewer, 22 seeds or 30 seeds?

| 22 | |
| 30 | |

TRY IT

Write Numerals From 1 Through 30

Trace and Show Numbers

Cut out each train card.

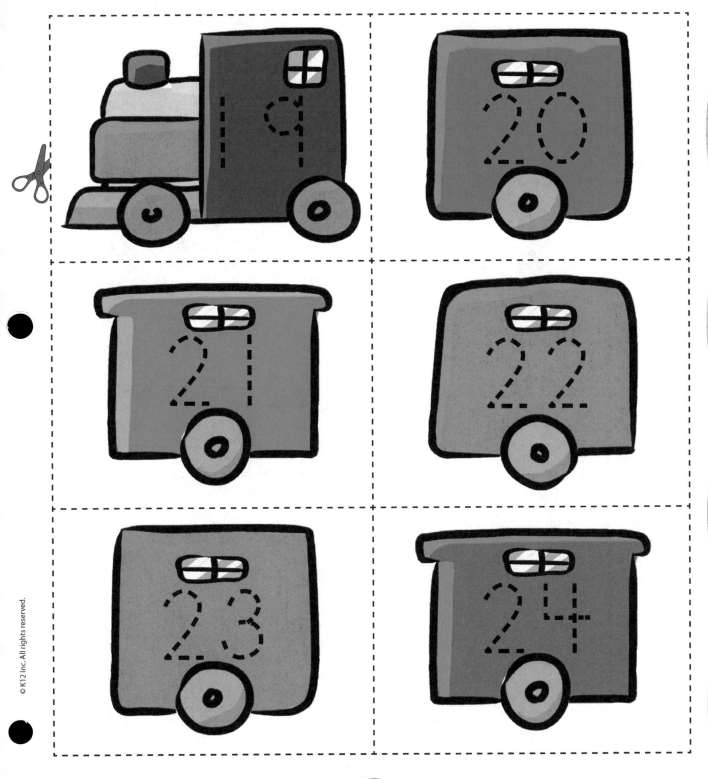

L E A R N

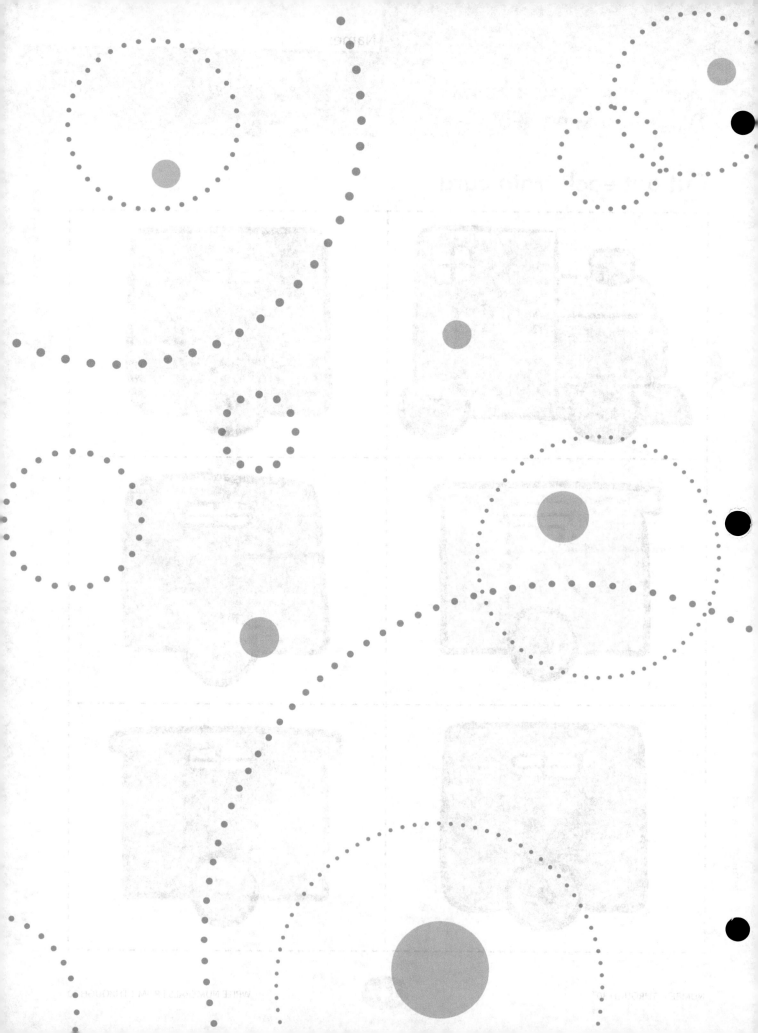

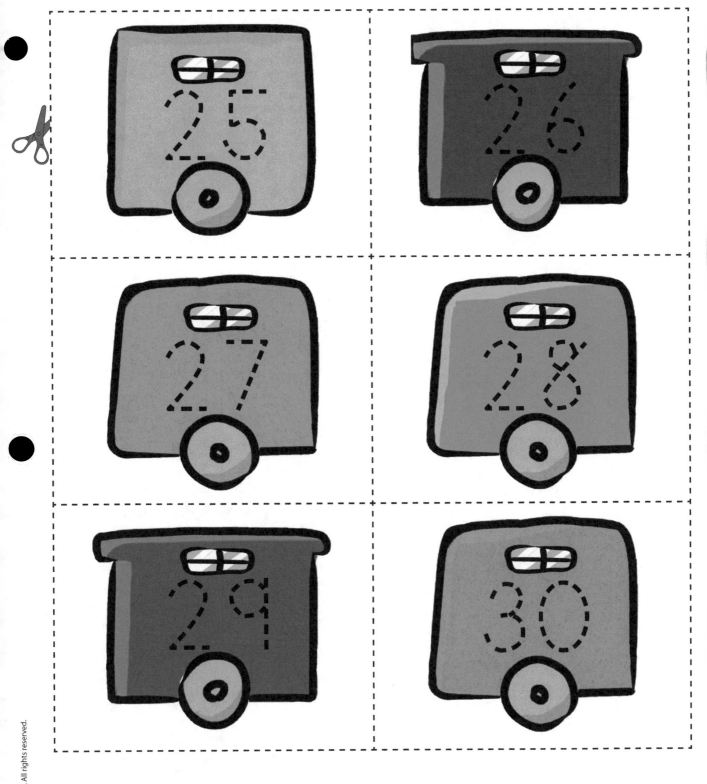

LEARN

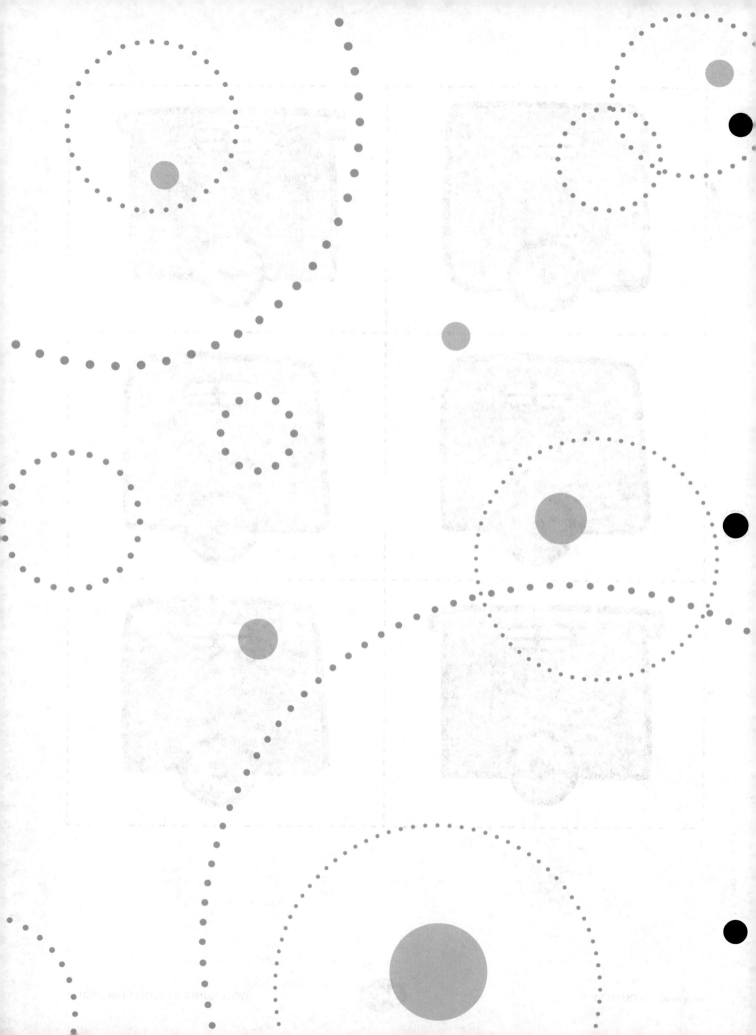

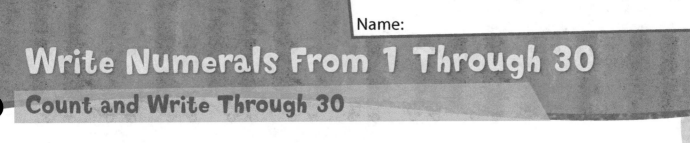

Write Numerals From 1 Through 30

Count and Write Through 30

Write the number of objects shown in the picture.

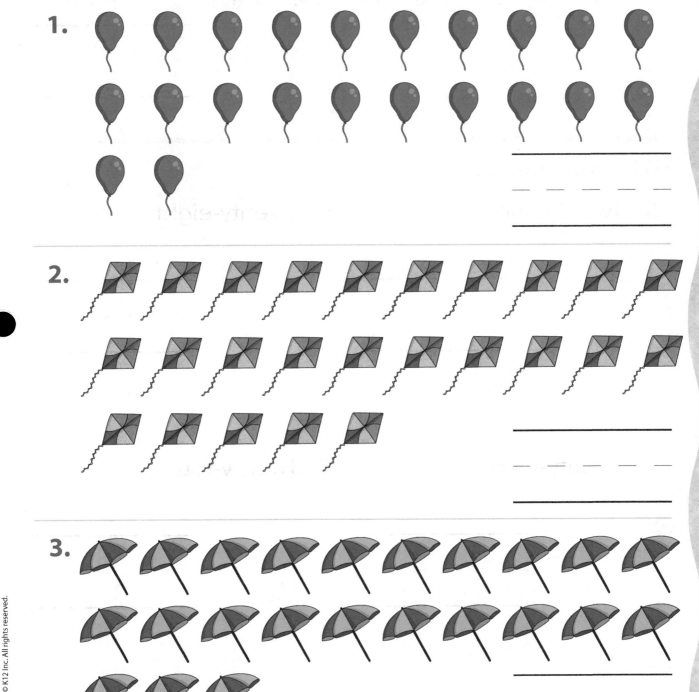

1.

2.

3.

TRY IT

Name:

4.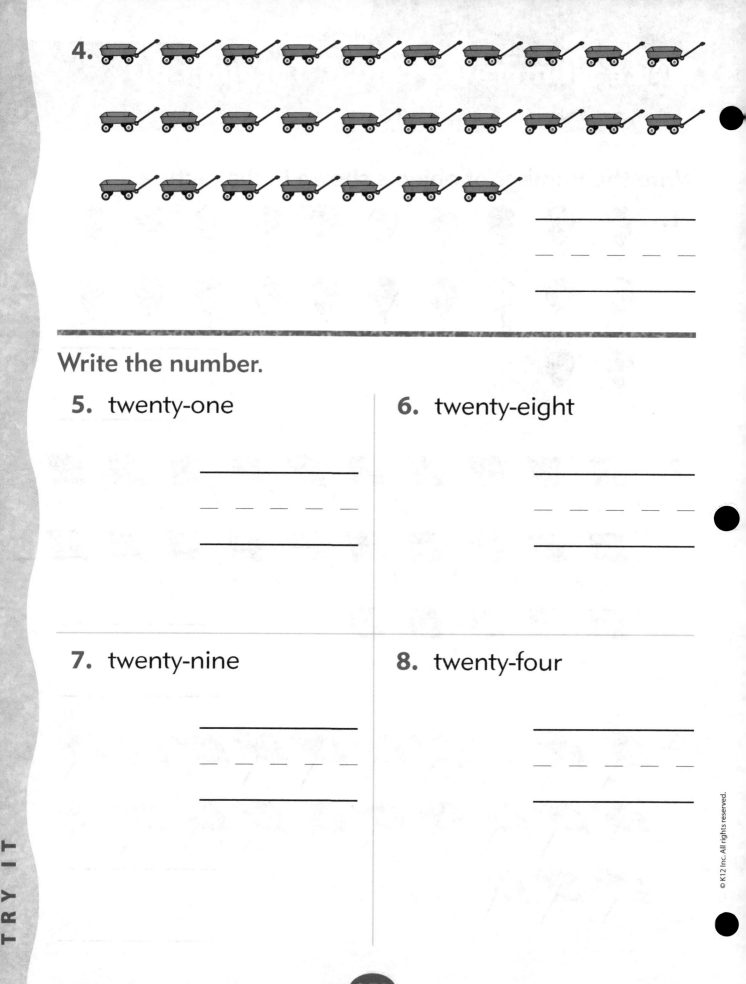

_____

- - - - - - - - -

_____

Write the number.

5. twenty-one

_____

- - - - - - - - -

_____

6. twenty-eight

_____

- - - - - - - - -

_____

7. twenty-nine

_____

- - - - - - - - -

_____

8. twenty-four

_____

- - - - - - - - -

_____

TRY IT

Name:

Count aloud the number of objects in the problem.

1. How many butterflies are there?

2. How many pieces of chalk are there?

3. How many fish are there?

Draw dots to show the number on the tile.

4.

23

5.

20

Circle the answer.
Count aloud to help you, if needed.

6. Which group has fewer flowers?

A. 20

B. 28

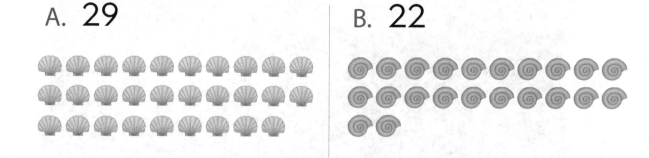

7. Which is more, 29 shells or 22 shells?

A. 29

B. 22

8. Which group of crayons is equal to the one below?

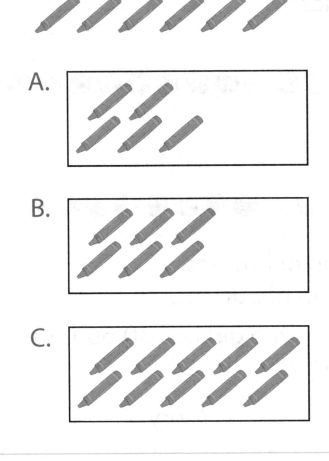

A.

B.

C.

---

9. Dave has 12 paintbrushes and Peg has 17. Who has more paintbrushes?

A. Dave

B. Peg

10. Jana has 28 marbles. Sam has 17 marbles.
Who has more marbles?

A. Jana

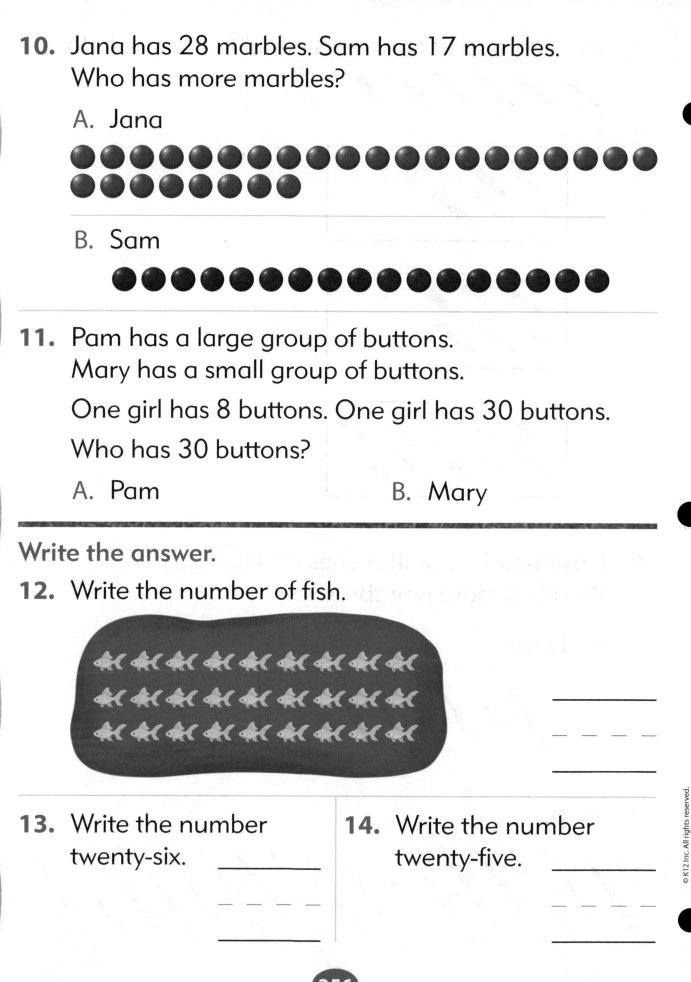

B. Sam

11. Pam has a large group of buttons.
Mary has a small group of buttons.

One girl has 8 buttons. One girl has 30 buttons.

Who has 30 buttons?

A. Pam   B. Mary

Write the answer.

12. Write the number of fish.

_____

- - - - - - -

_____

13. Write the number
twenty-six. _____

- - - - - - -

_____

14. Write the number
twenty-five. _____

- - - - - - -

_____

Identify Solid Figures

Making Paper Cones

Follow the directions to make three paper cones.

Step 1

Cut out the three-sided shape (Figure 1). Cut only on the dotted lines. You will use this shape to form the cone.

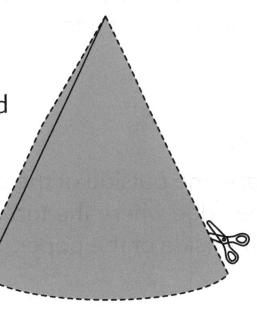

Figure 1

Step 2

Fold along the solid line to make a tab (Figure 2).

Figure 2

LEARN

Step 3

Turn the shape with your hands until the tab meets the other side of the paper (Figure 3). Tuck the tab under the other side. You now have a paper cone.

Step 4

Tape the outside of the cone along the edge where the tab meets the other side of the paper.

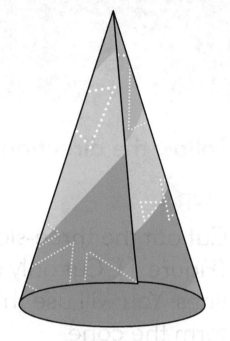

Figure 3

Step 5

Cut out the circle.

Step 6

Tape the circle over the circular opening of the cone (Figure 4).

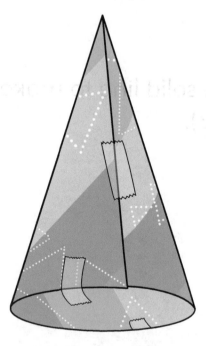

Figure 4

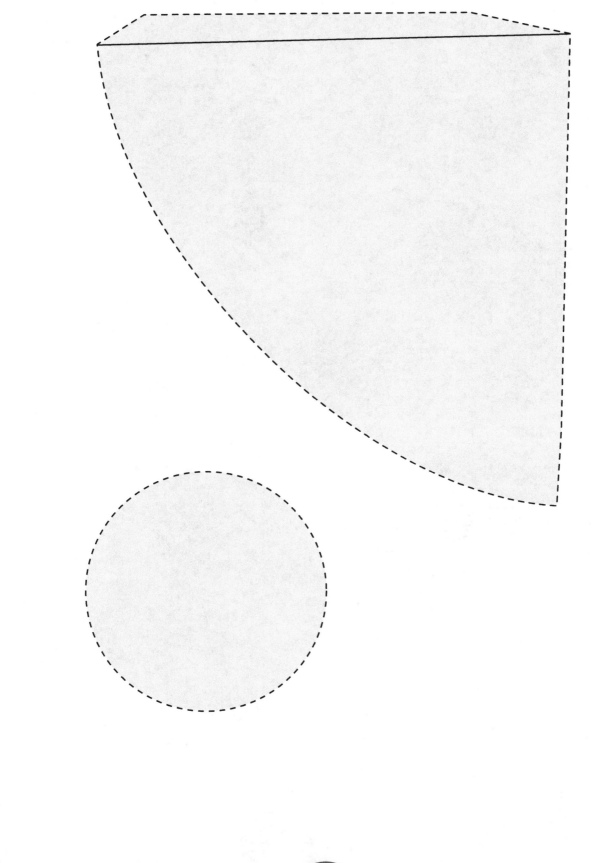

LEARN

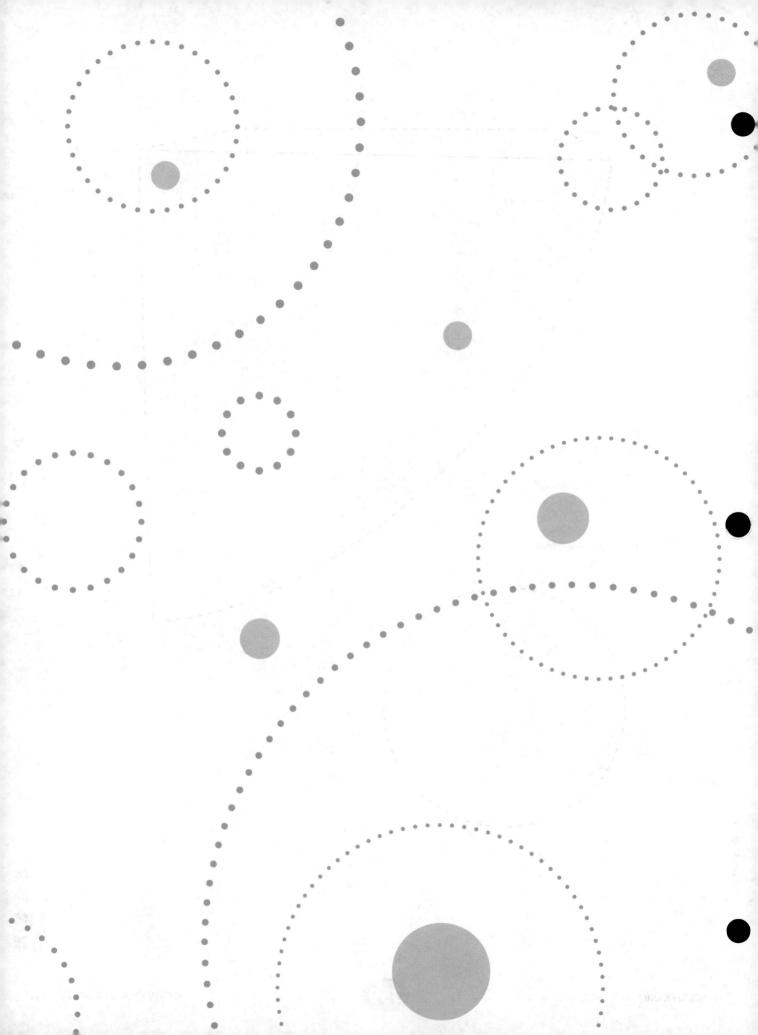

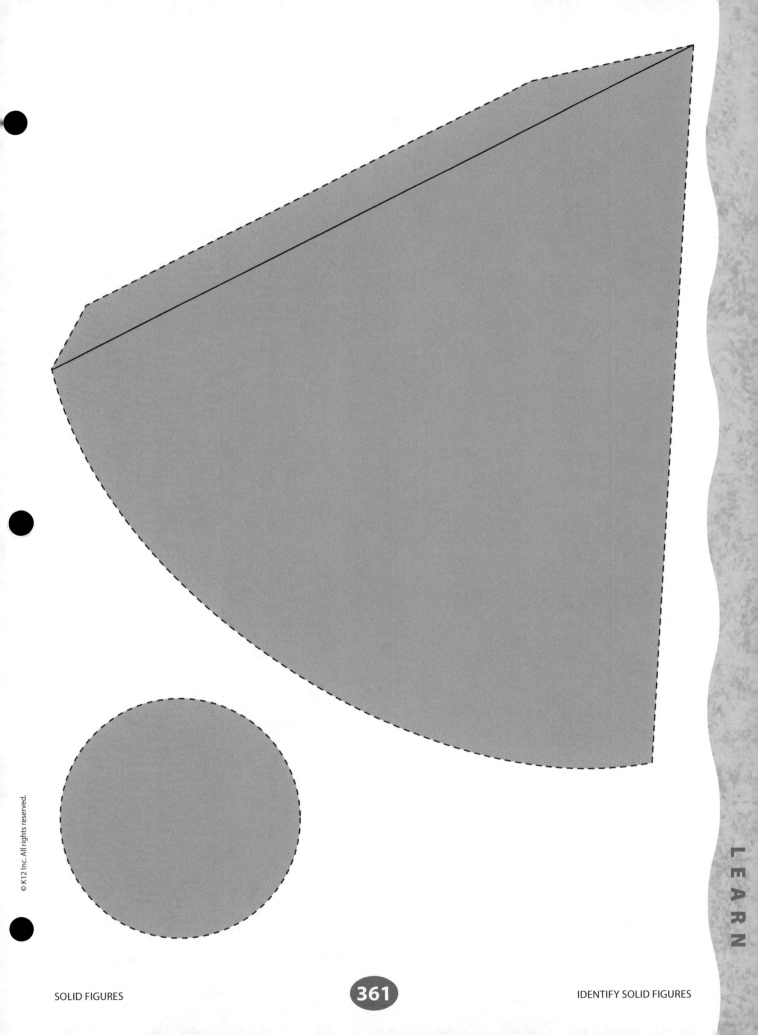

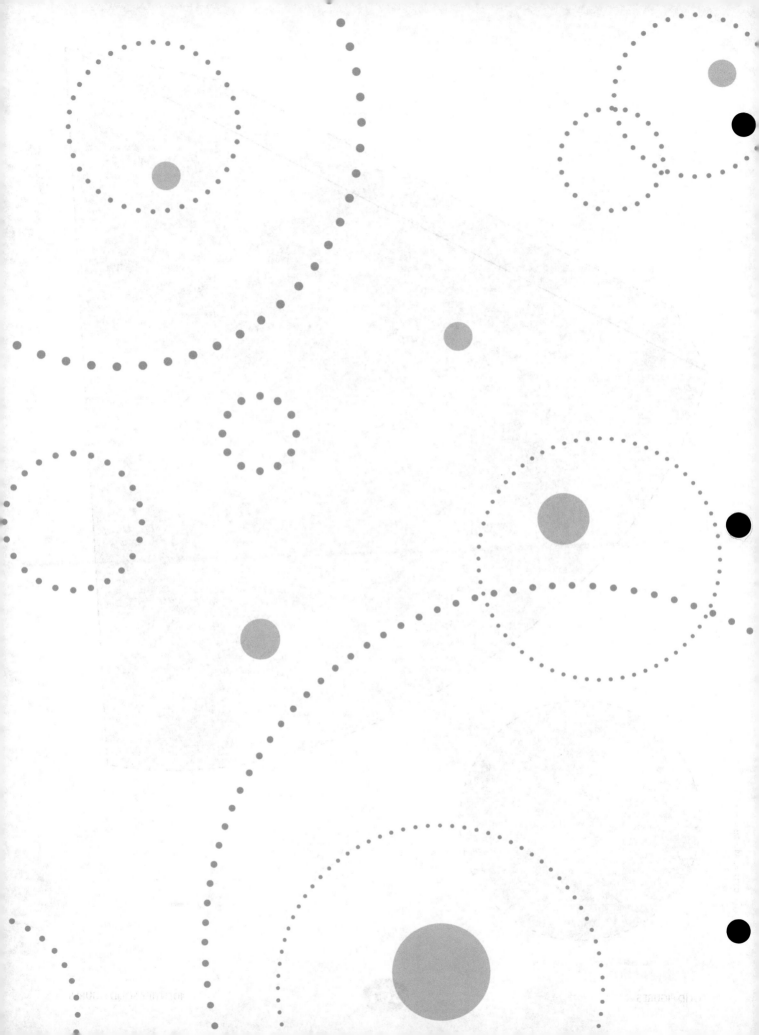

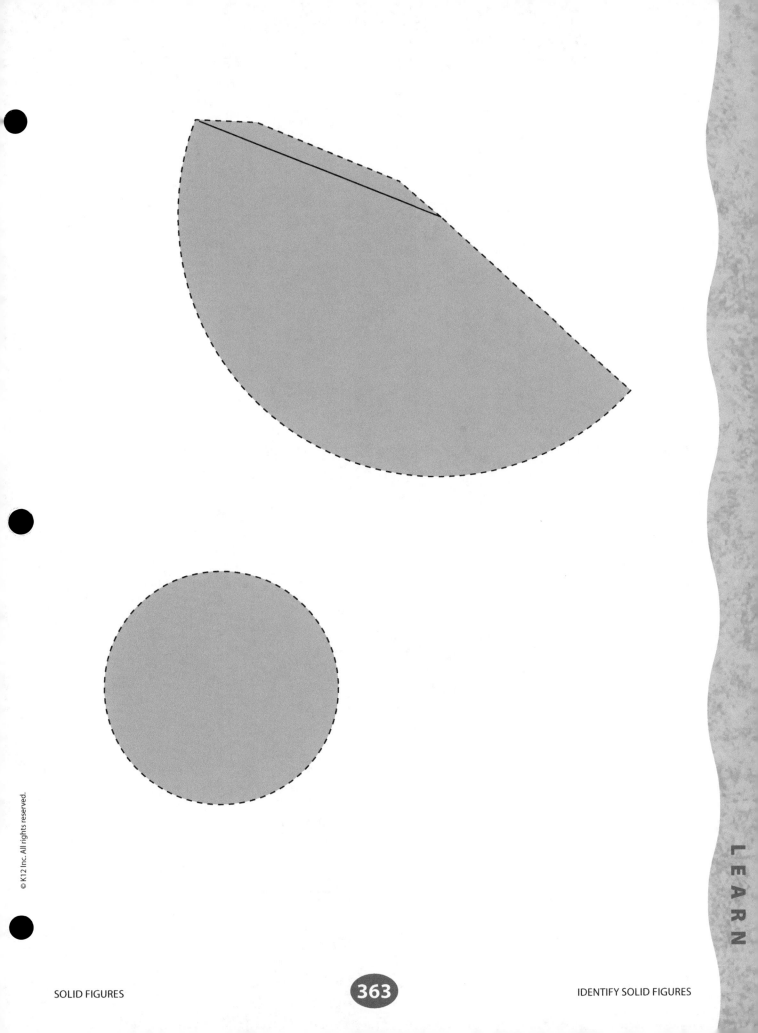

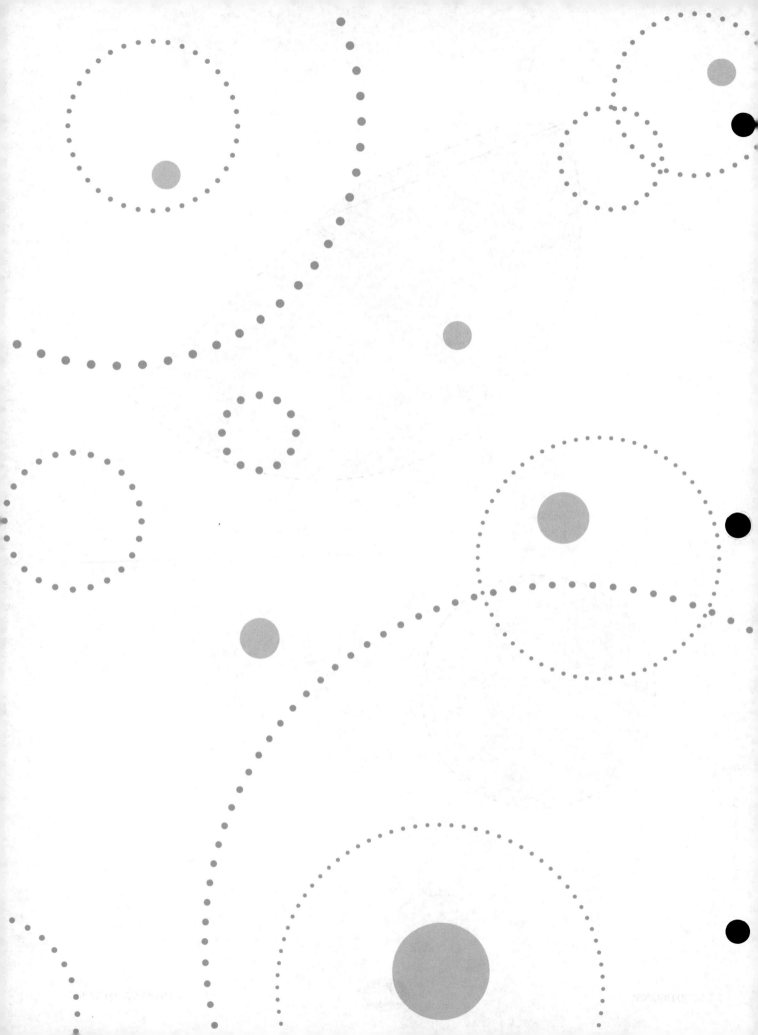

Identify Solid Figures

Identify Solids

Trace one side of the solid. Circle the name of the shape that you see.

1. cube

2. cone

A. square	A. square
B. triangle	B. triangle
C. circle	C. circle

Circle the answer.

3. Which is a cube?

A.
B.
C.

TRY IT

4. Which is a sphere?

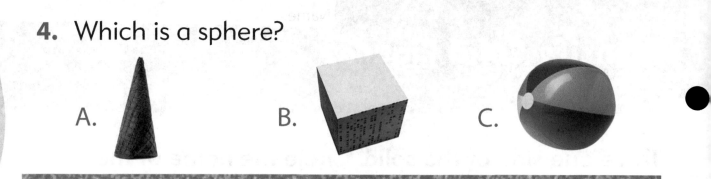

A.   B.   C.

Look at the solids and follow the directions.

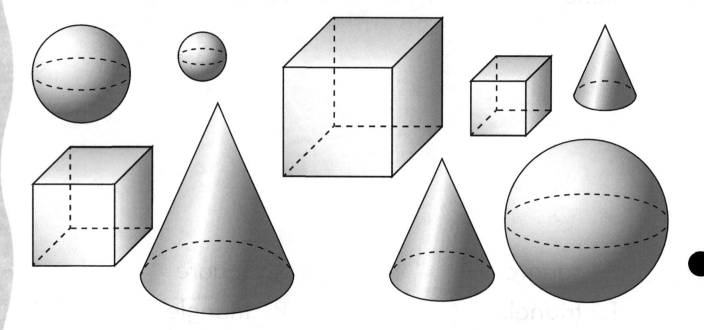

5. Color all the cubes red.

6. Color all the spheres green.

7. Color all the cones blue.

Circle the answer.

8. Which is a cone?

A.    B.    C.

TRY IT

Solid Figures: More Exploration

Extend Your Understanding

Put the blocks in a row in front of you. Use the blocks to answer Problems 1–9.

1. Point to the sphere.

2. Point to the cube

3. Point to the cone.

4. Pick up the cube. Tell what shape you see on each side.

5. Pick up the cone. Tell what shape you see on the flat side.

6. Pick up the block that looks most like a ball.

7. Pick up the block that looks most like an ice-cream cone.

8. Pick up the block that looks most like a toy building block.

9. Put the blocks in this order: sphere, cube, cone.

REVIEW

Use crayons to answer Problems 10–12.

10. Color the cube.

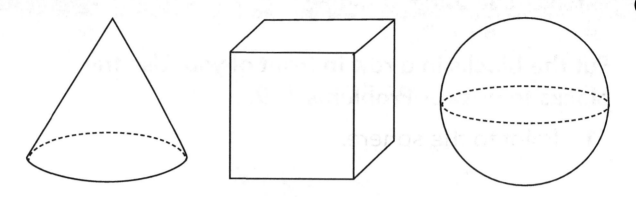

11. Color the sphere.

12. Color the cone.

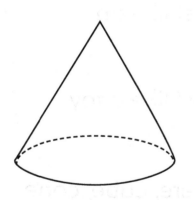
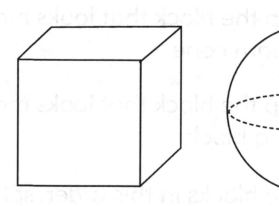
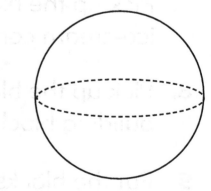

R E V I E W

Compare Solids by Shape or Size

Compare Solids by Size

Read the problem and follow the directions.

1. Circle the cube that is the smallest.

2. Draw an X on the sphere that is the largest.

3. Circle the cone that is the smallest.

L E A R N

4. Color the 2 balls that are the same size.

5. Draw an X on the 2 presents that are the same size.

6. Circle the 2 ice-cream cones that are the same size.

LEARN

Compare Figures by Shape or Size

Compare Solids

Read the problem and follow the directions.

1. Draw an X on the cube that is the largest.

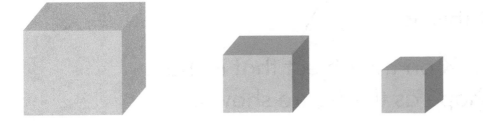

2. Circle the cone that is the smallest.

3. Color the sphere that is largest.

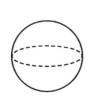
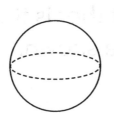
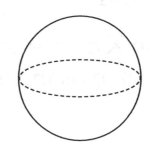

T R Y   I T

4. Color the 2 cubes that are the same size.

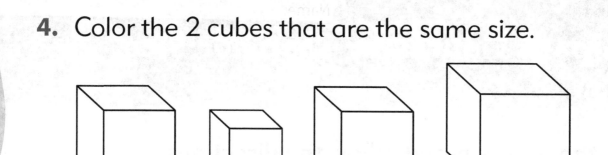

5. Look at this figure.

Draw an X on the object that is the same shape as the figure shown.

6. Look at this figure.

Circle the object that is the same shape as the figure shown.

7. Look at this figure.

Draw an X on the object that is the same shape as the figure shown.

T R Y   I T

Name:

Attributes: More Exploration

Extend Your Understanding

Put the blocks in a row in front of you. Use the blocks to answer Problems 1–6.

1. Pick up the block that has no corners.

2. Pick up the block that has square sides.

3. Pick up the block that has 8 corners.

4. Pick up the block that has a circle for a side.

5. Pick up 2 blocks that can roll.

6. Pick up the block that has only one corner.

REVIEW

Circle the answer or answers.

7. Which block is largest?

A.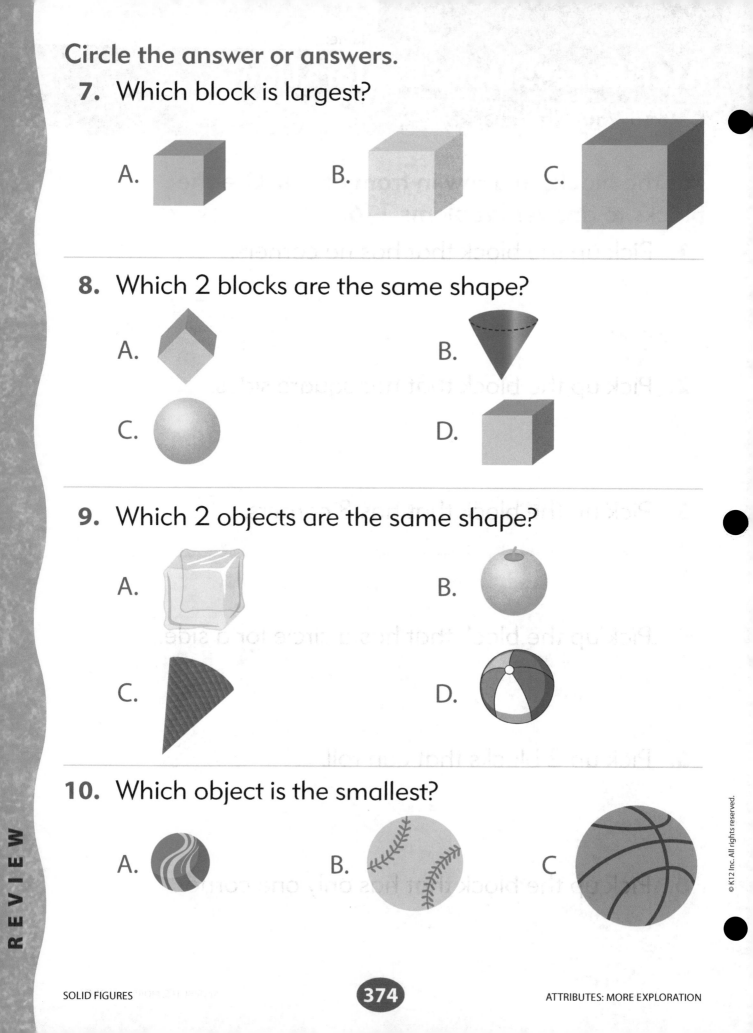

B.

C.

8. Which 2 blocks are the same shape?

A.

B.

C.

D.

9. Which 2 objects are the same shape?

A.

B.

C.

D.

10. Which object is the smallest?

A.

B.

C

Sort Solid Figures
Which Does Not Belong?

Compare the color, shape, and size of the solid figures in the problem. Draw an X on the solid figure that does **not** belong in the group.

1.

2.

3.

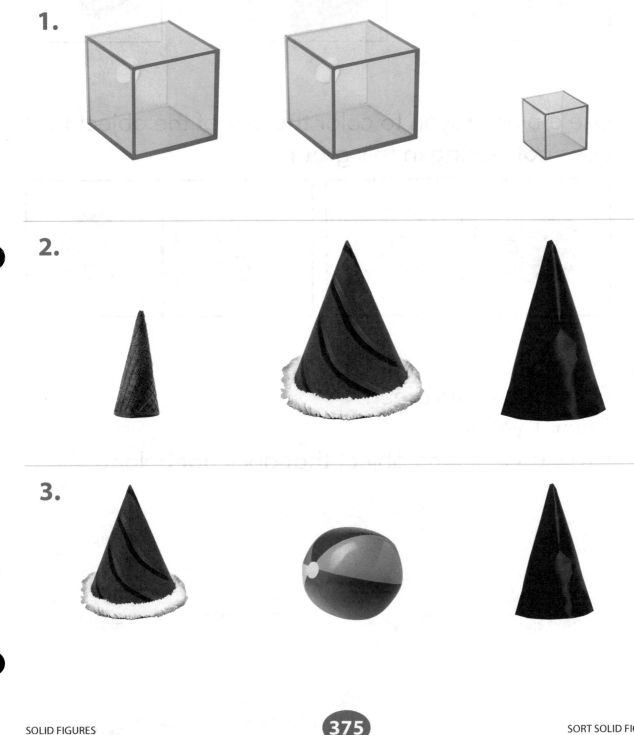

L E A R N

Compare the solid figures in the problem.

4. Use a green crayon to color the box of the object that does **not** belong in this group.

5. Use a blue crayon to color the box of the object that does **not** belong in this group.

6. Color 3 spheres green.
Color 1 yellow.
Draw an X on the object that does **not** belong.

Sort Solid Figures
Identify the Different Solid Figure

Compare the solid figures in the group.
Draw an X on the object that does **not** belong
in the group. Circle what makes it different—
its color, shape, or size.

1.

A. shape   B. size

2.

A. color   B. size

3.

A. shape   B. size

TRY IT

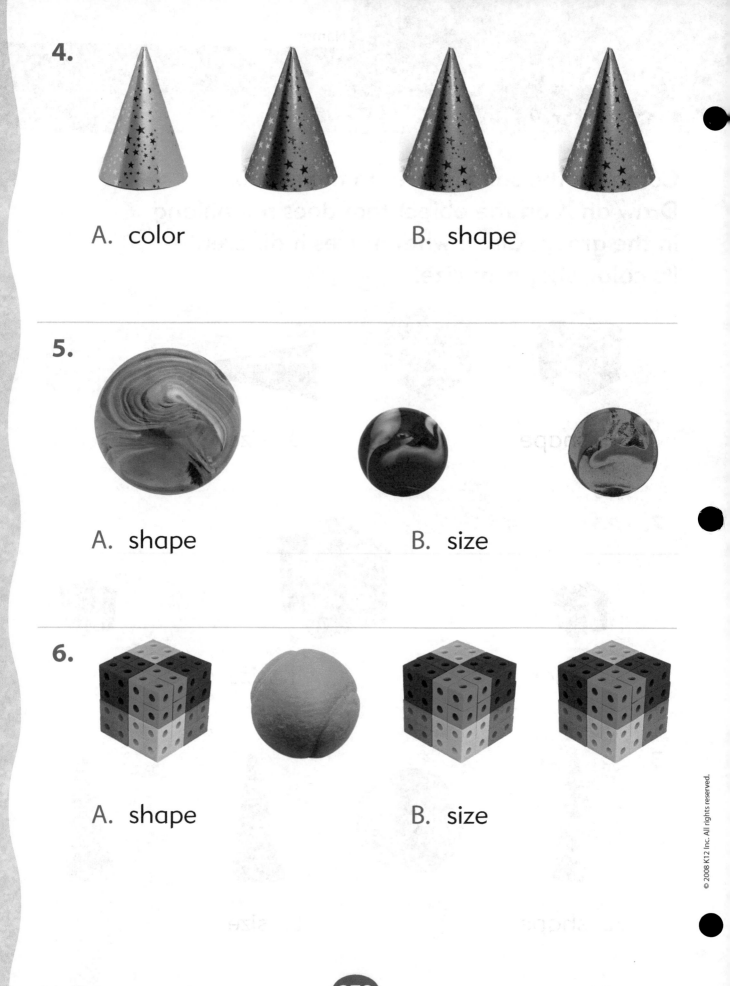

4.

A. color   B. shape

5.

A. shape   B. size

6.

A. shape   B. size

Put Together Shapes
Create Different Shapes

Use the blocks and cut-out circles. Read the problem and circle the answer.

1. Put these shapes together.

Which shape can be made?

A. ◣   B. ⬤   C. ◼

2. Put these shapes together.

Which shape can be made?

A. ▬   B. ⬤   C. ◼

T R Y   I T

3. Put these shapes together.

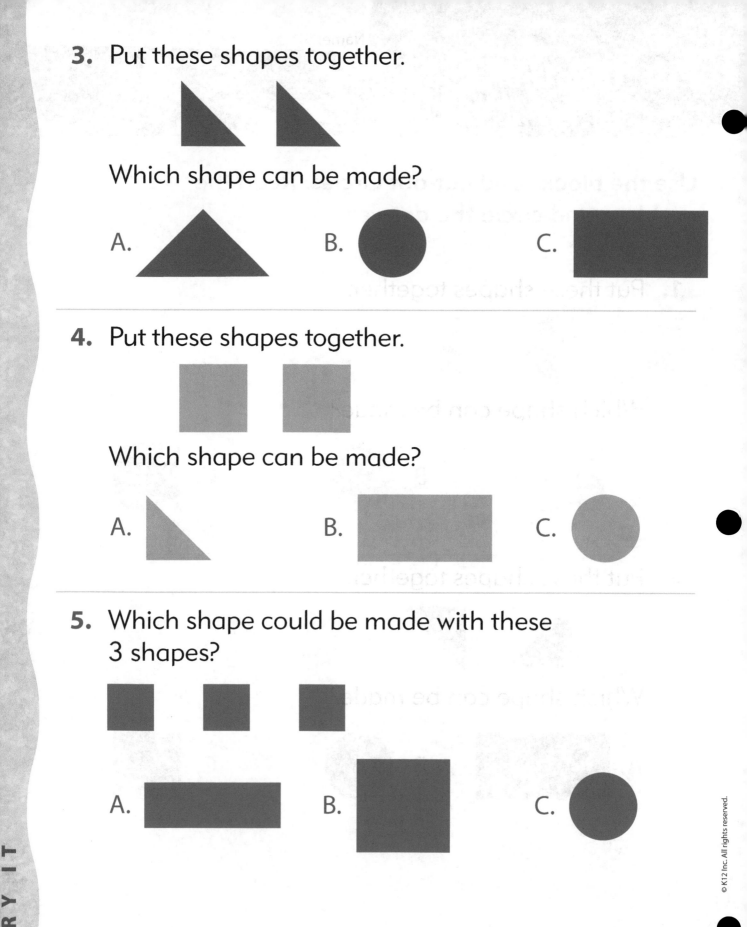

Which shape can be made?

A.

B.

C.

4. Put these shapes together.

Which shape can be made?

A.

B.

C.

5. Which shape could be made with these 3 shapes?

A.

B.

C.

T R Y   I T

6. Which shape could be made by putting these 4 shapes together?

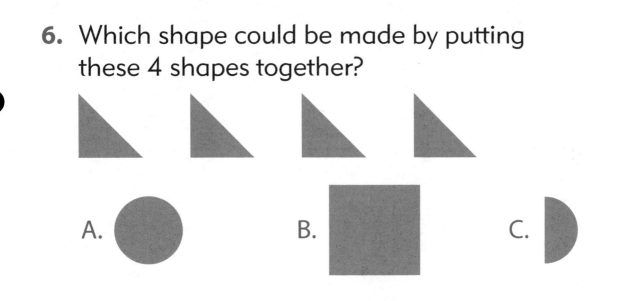

A. B. C.

Use the blocks to make the shape.

7. Put 4 triangles together to make a square. Then put 4 triangles together to make a rectangle.

T R Y   I T

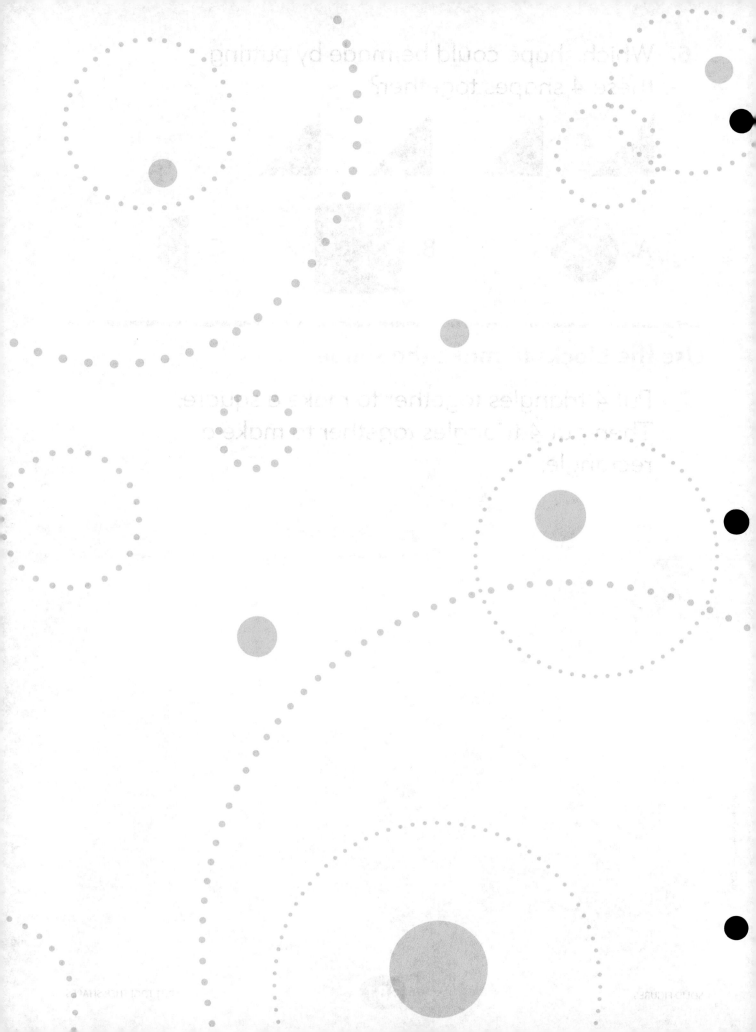

Name:

Take Apart Shapes
Cut Up Shapes

Cut each shape and make different shapes.

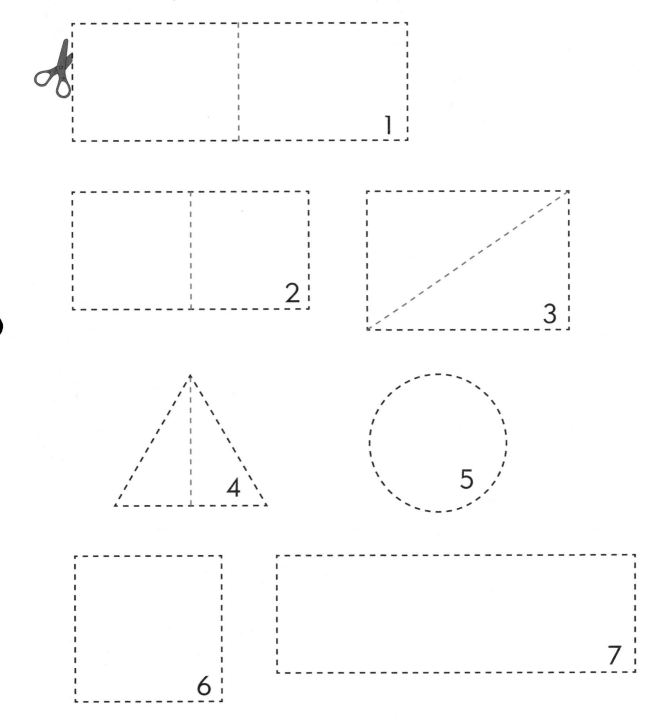

383

L E A R N

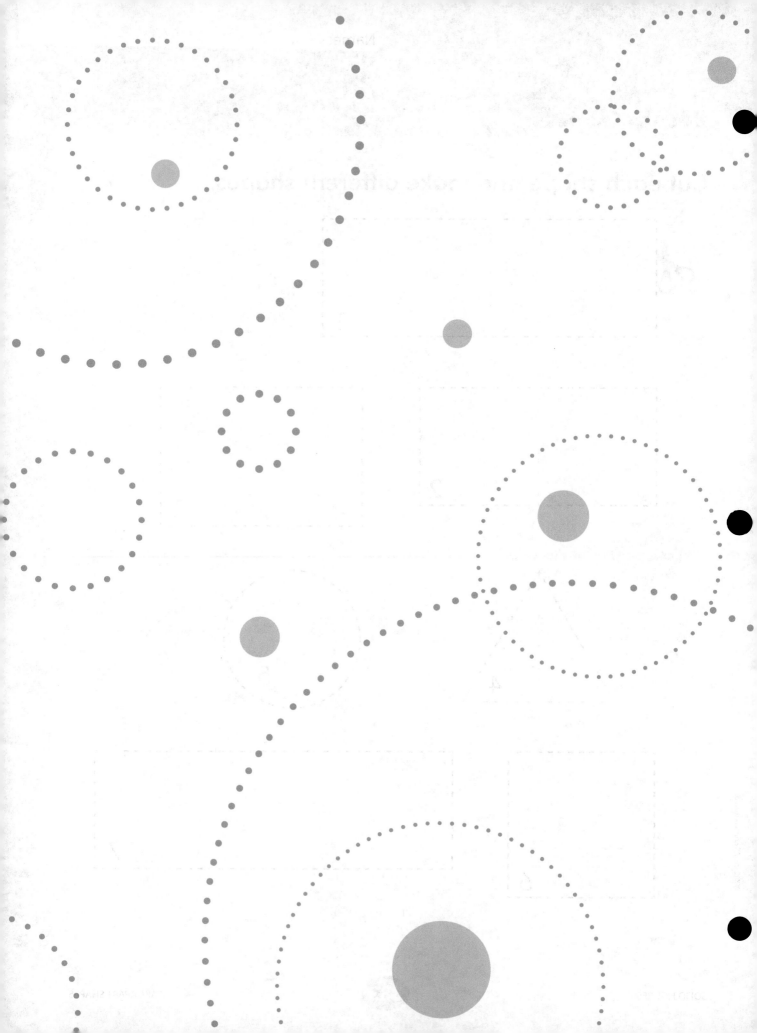

Take Apart Shapes
Separate Shapes with Lines

Draw a line or lines to show how to break apart the shape.

1. Make 2 triangles.

2. Make 2 rectangles.

3. Make 4 smaller squares.

4. Make 4 rectangles.

5. Make 2 new shapes that are the same size.

6. Make 4 new shapes that are the same size.

LEARN

7. Make 2 squares.

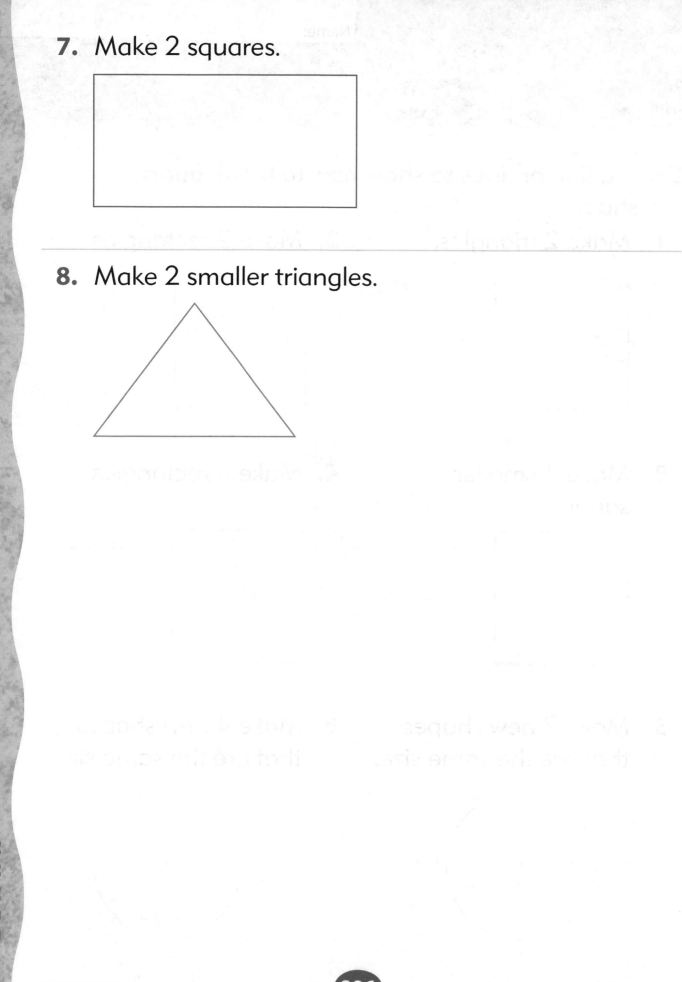

8. Make 2 smaller triangles.

L E A R N

Take Apart Shapes
Shapes Within Shapes

The first picture shows one way to break apart the shape. Draw 1 line or more than 1 line to show a different way to break apart the shape.

1.
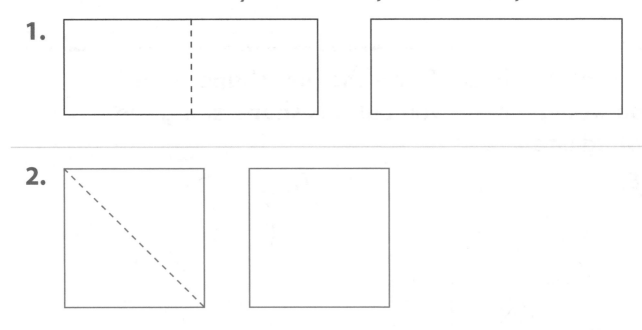

2.

Draw a line or lines to show how to break apart the shape.

3. Make 2 rectangles.

T R Y   I T

4. Make 2 rectangles.

5. Make 2 triangles.

Look at the shape. Circle the new shapes that you would make if you cut this shape along the dotted line.

6.

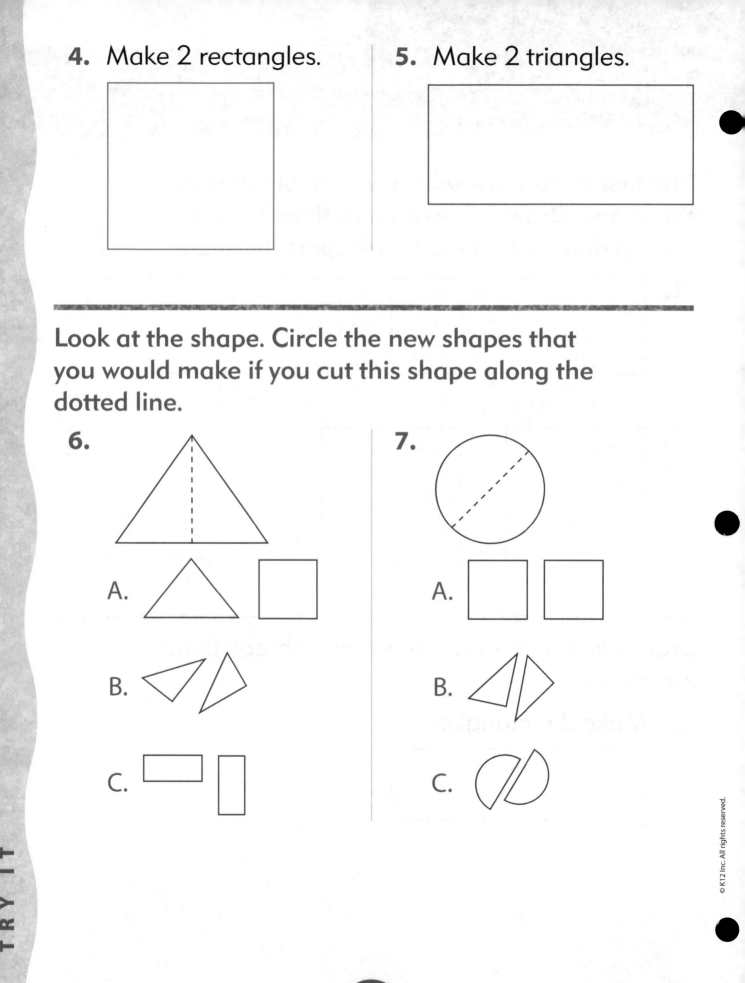

A.

B.

C.

7.

A.

B.

C.

TRY IT

Use scissors to answer the problem.

8. Cut apart the square to make 4 smaller shapes. Tell what shapes you made.

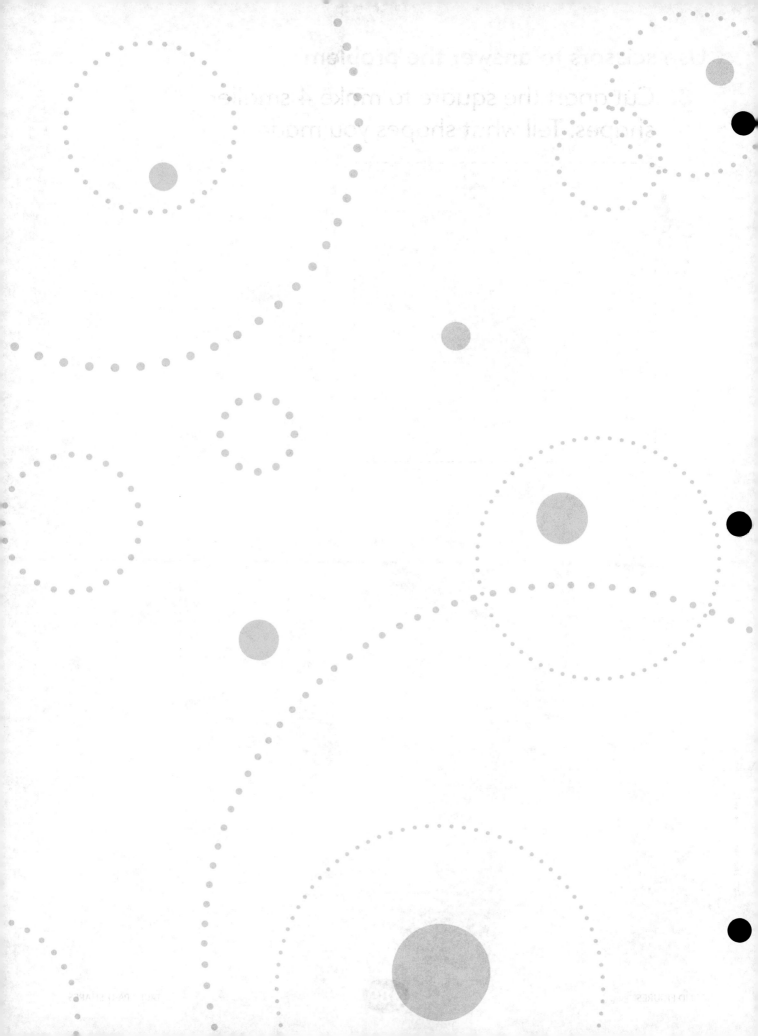

Unit Review

Checkpoint Practice

Read the problem and follow the directions.

1. Circle the object that is shaped like a sphere.

2. Circle the 2 cone-shaped objects that are the same size.

3. Draw an X on the object that does **not** belong.

4. Circle the shape you can make if you put together these shapes.

5. Draw a line on the square to make 2 triangles.

6. Circle the figure that **is the smallest** in this group.

7. Draw an X over the figure that is the smallest.

UNIT REVIEW

Circle the answer.

8. Sarah is collecting green objects. Which object does **not** belong in her collection?

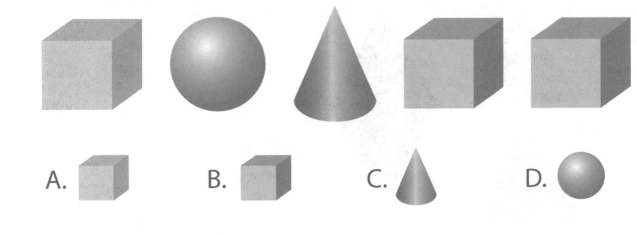

A.    B.    C.   D.

---

9. Which is a cube?

A.   B.   C.

---

10. Which looks like a sphere?

A.   B.   C.

---

11. Which **2** spheres are the same size?

A.   B.   C.   D.

Use blocks to solve Problems 12 and 13.

12. Put the 2 triangles and the rhombus together to make a larger triangle.

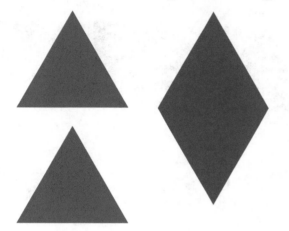

13. Put the 3 squares together. Circle the shape you can make.

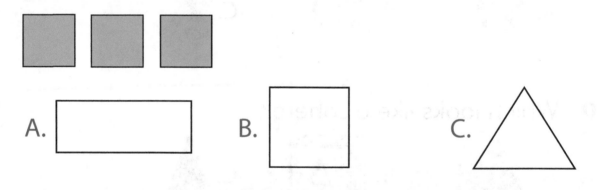

A. B. C.

Use a ruler or straight edge for Problem 14.

14. Draw a straight line through this rectangle to make 2 rectangles or 2 squares.

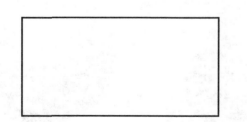

UNIT REVIEW

Centimeter Grid Paper

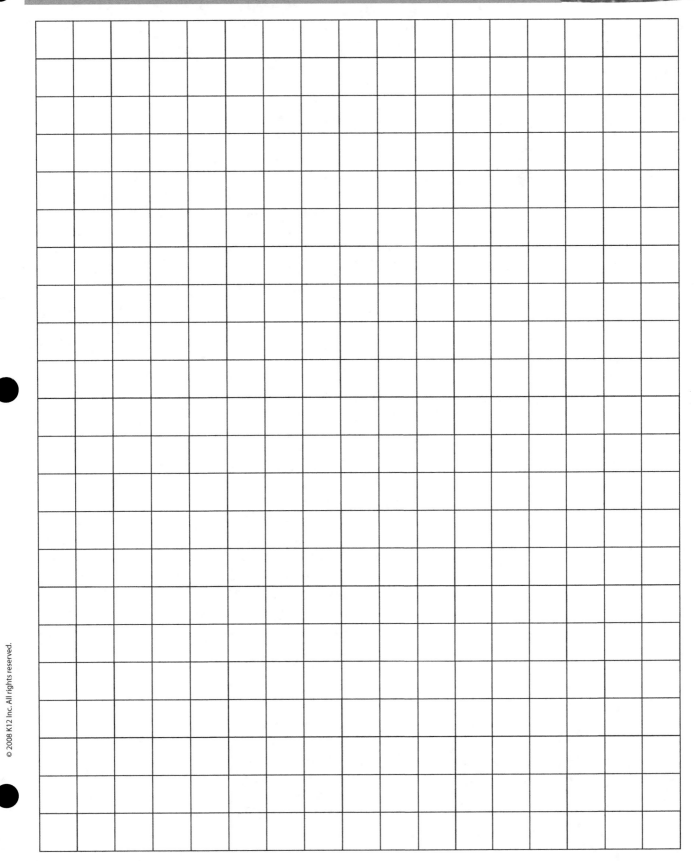

Circle Pieces

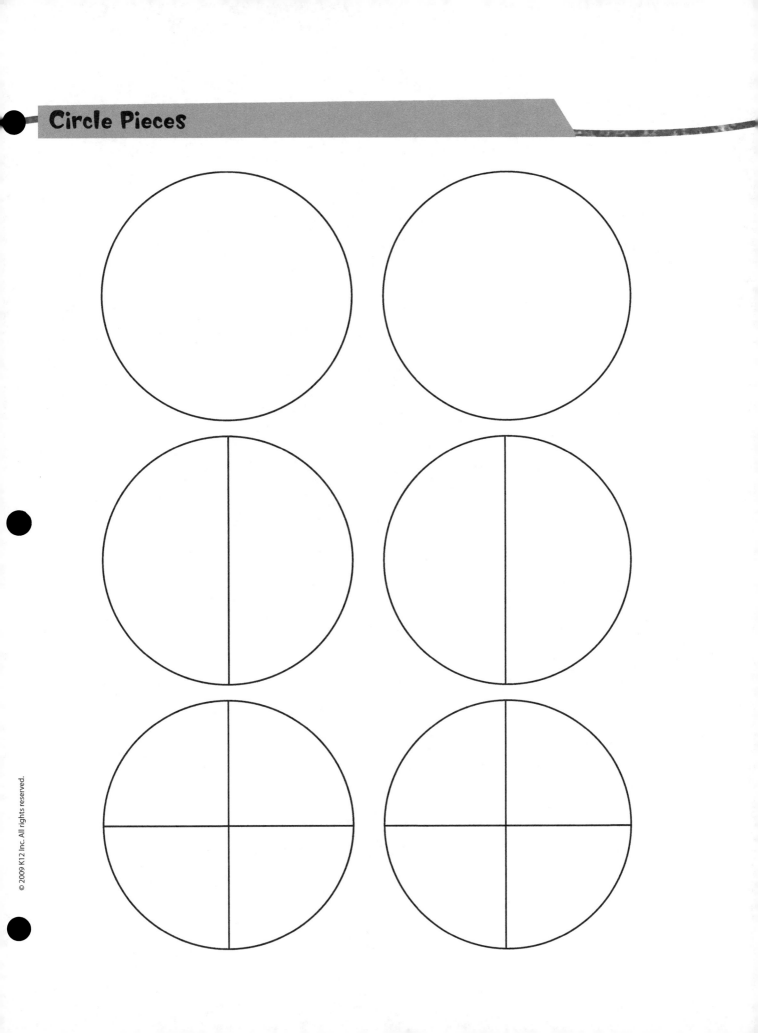

Domino Tiles

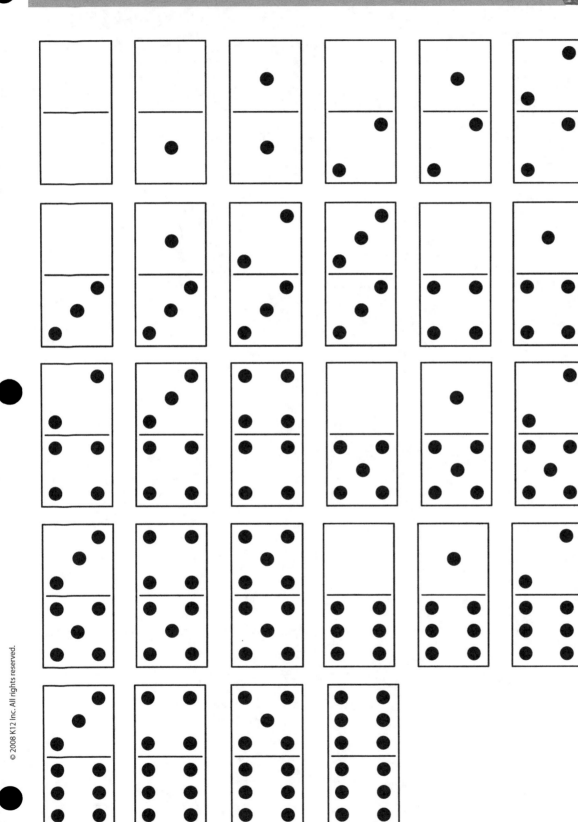

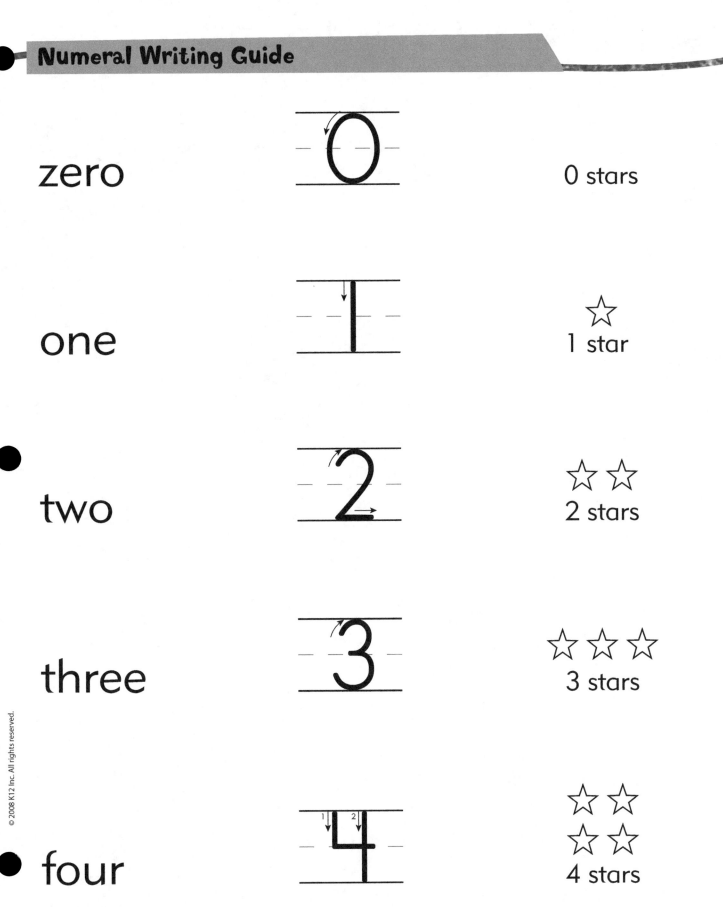

zero — 0 stars

one — 1 star

two — 2 stars

three — 3 stars

four — 4 stars

five

5 stars

six

6 stars

seven

7 stars

eight

8 stars

nine

9 stars

Numeral Writing Guide

0 zero

0 stars

Practice writing 0. Begin at the dot.

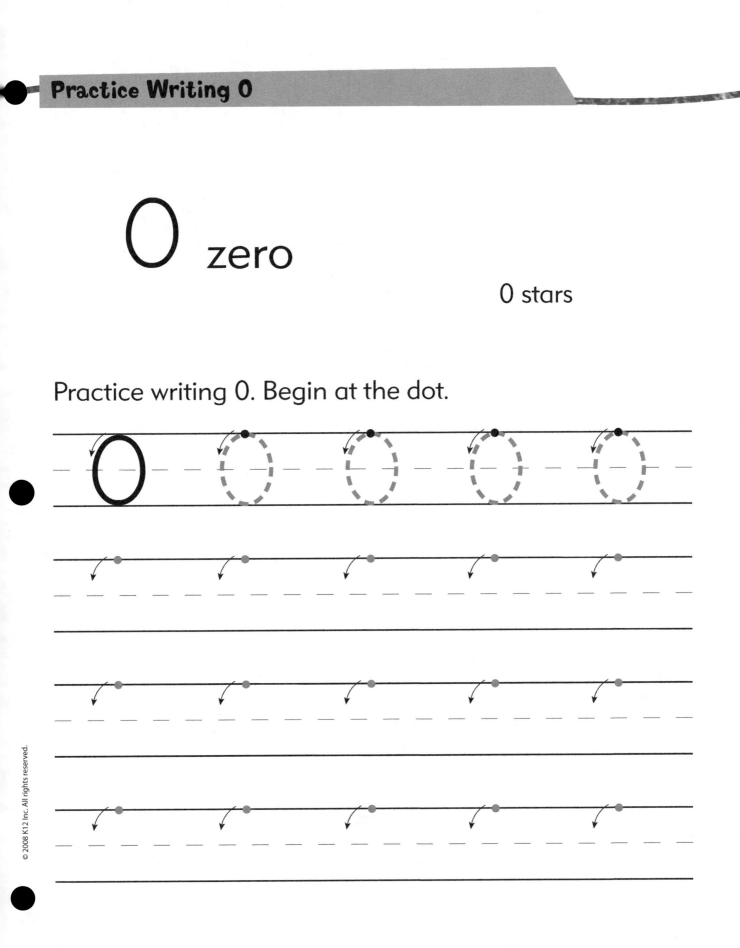

| one

☆
1 star

Practice writing 1. Begin at the dot.

2 two

2 stars

Practice writing 2. Begin at the dot.

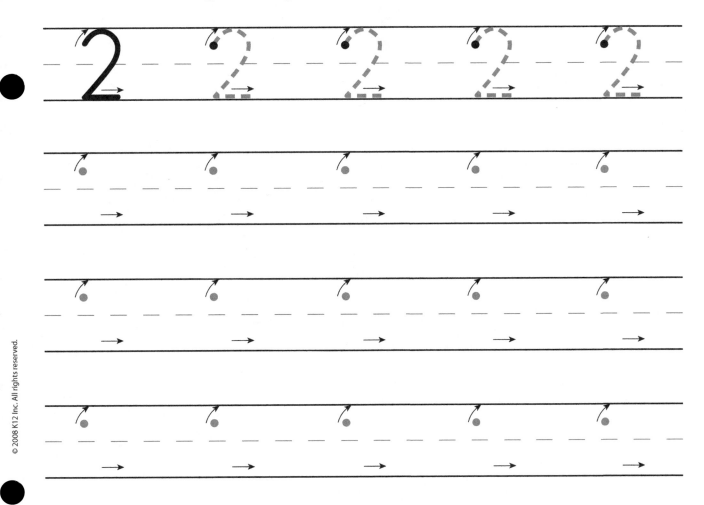

3 three

3 stars

Practice writing 3. Begin at the dot.

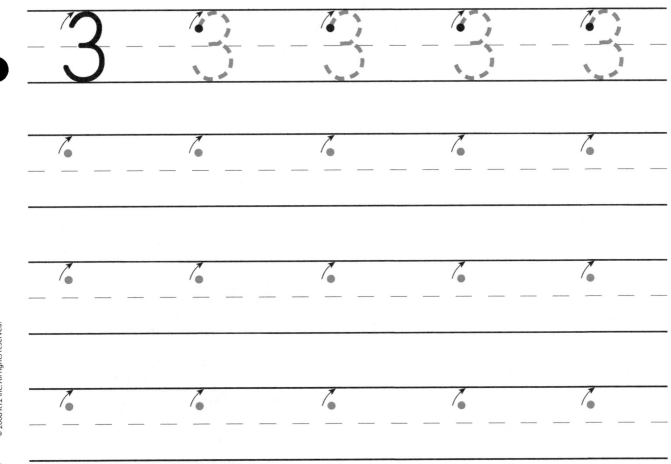

4 four

4 stars

Practice writing 4. Begin at the dot.

4 four

4 stars

Practice writing 4. Begin at the dot.

5 five

5 stars

Practice writing 5. Begin at the dot.

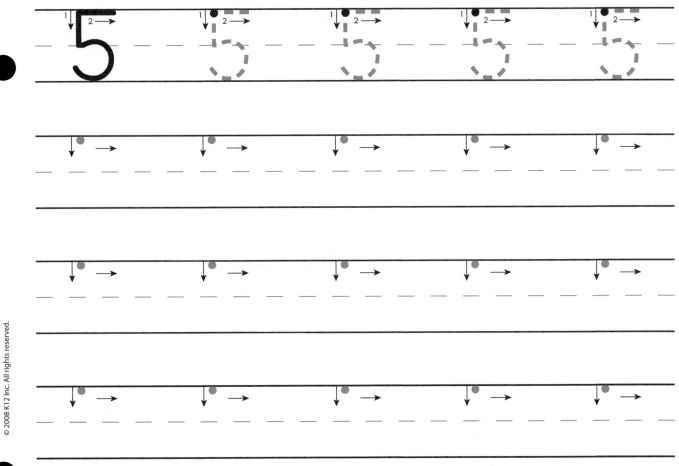

6 six

6 stars

Practice writing 6. Begin at the dot.

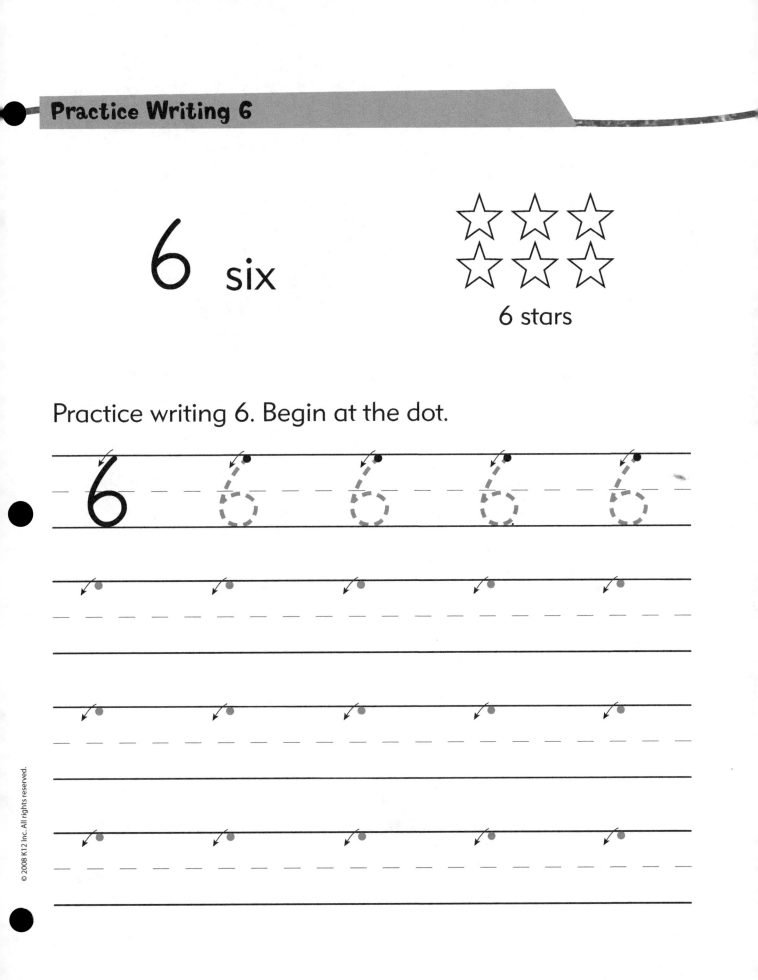

7 seven

7 stars

Practice writing 7. Begin at the dot.

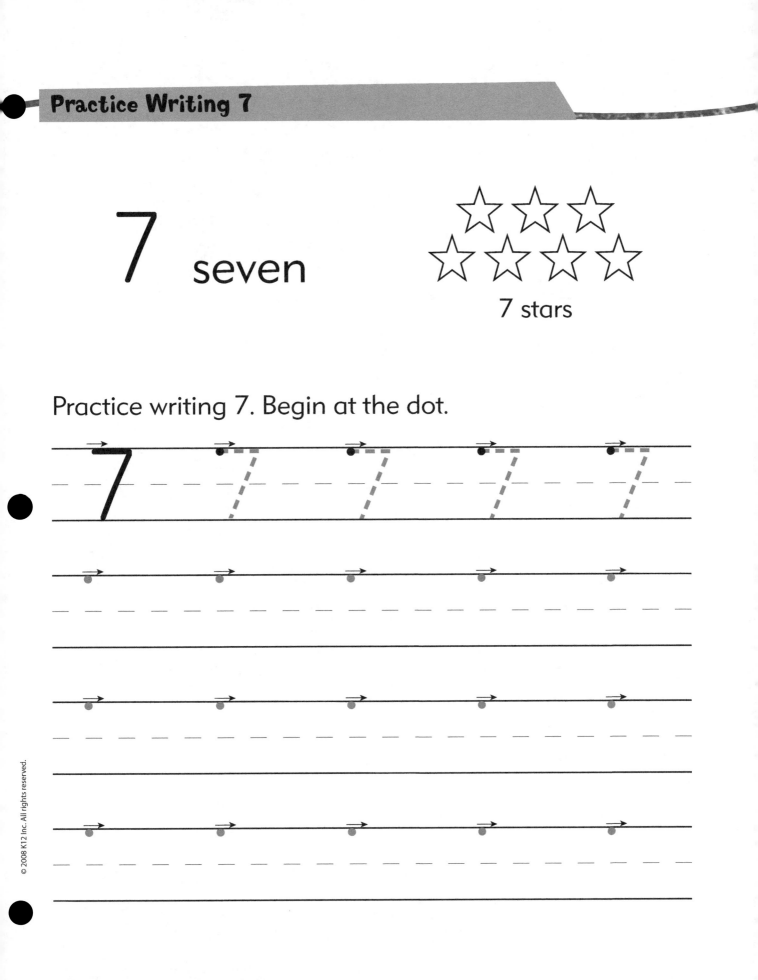

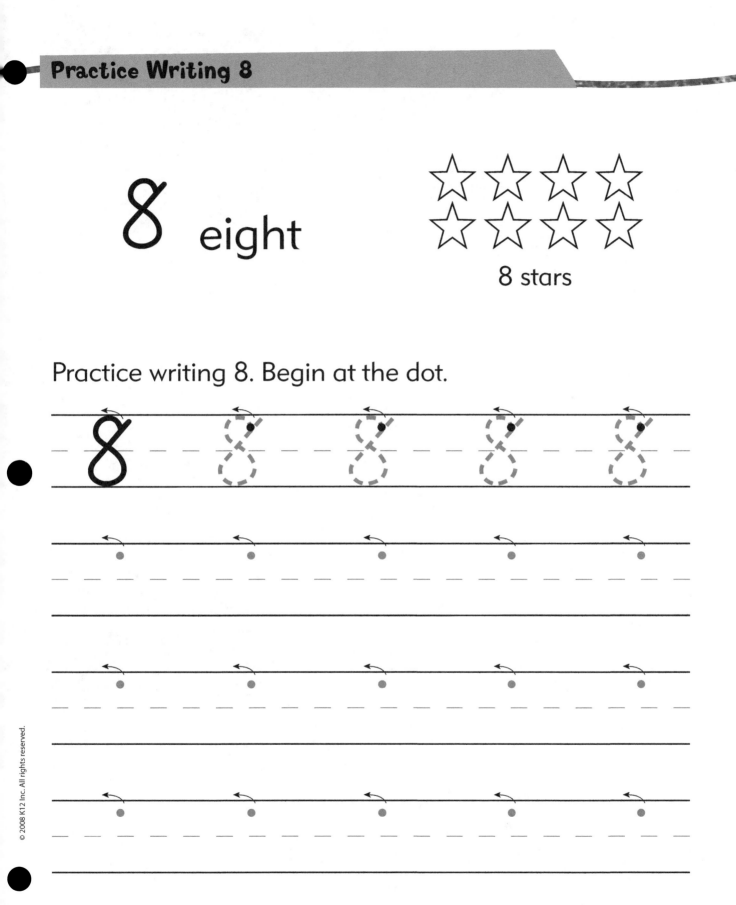

8 eight

8 stars

Practice writing 8. Begin at the dot.

9 nine

9 stars

Practice writing 9. Begin at the dot.

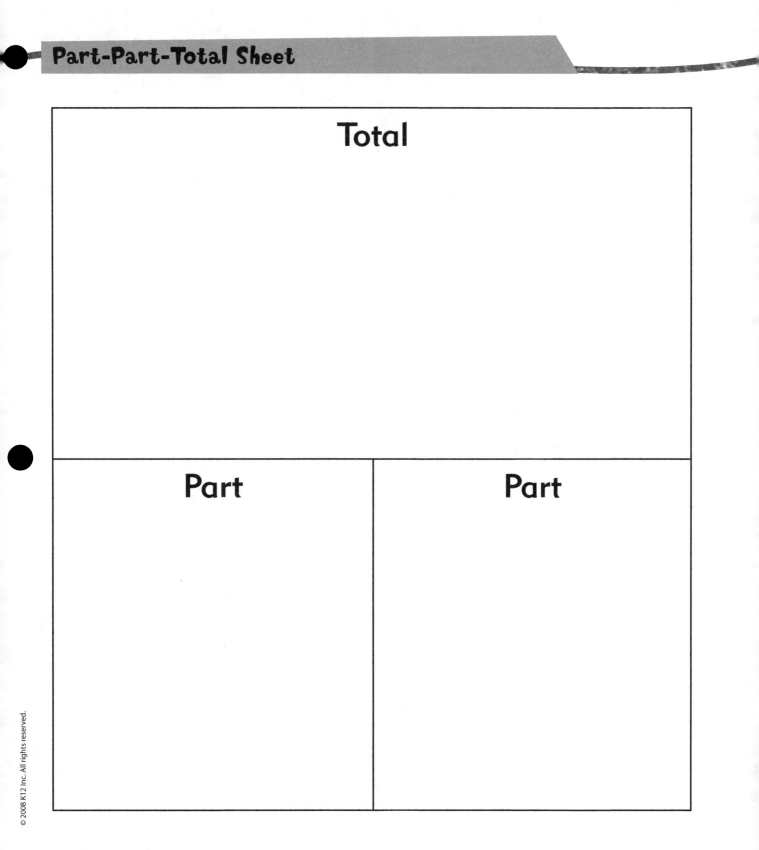

Total

Part

Part

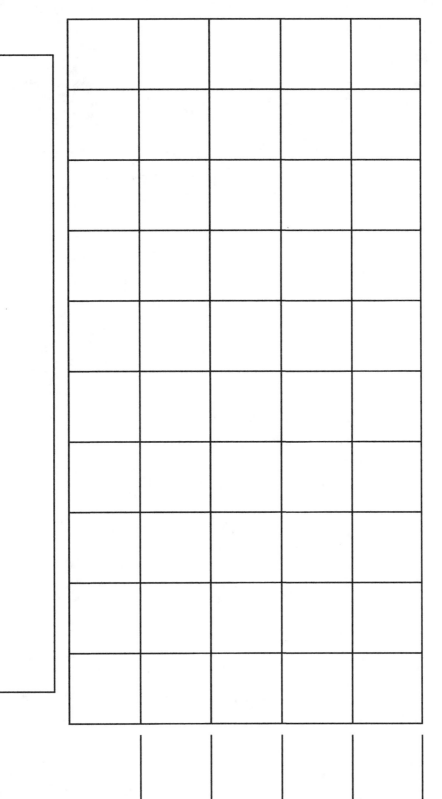

Each picture in the boxes equals 1.